THE PHYSIOLOGICAL EFFECTS OF EXERCISE PROGRAMS ON ADULTS

Publication Number 728

AMERICAN LECTURE SERIES®

A Monograph in

The BANNERSTONE DIVISION *of*
AMERICAN LECTURES IN SPORTSMEDICINE

Edited by

ERNST JOKL, M.D.
University of Kentucky
Lexington, Kentucky

THE PHYSIOLOGICAL EFFECTS OF EXERCISE PROGRAMS ON ADULTS

Second Printing

By

THOMAS KIRK CURETON, Ph.D., F.A.C.S.M.

Physical Fitness Research Laboratory
University of Illinois
Urbana, Illinois

CHARLES C THOMAS • PUBLISHER
Springfield · Illinois · U.S.A.

Published and Distributed Throughout the World by

CHARLES C THOMAS • PUBLISHER

BANNERSTONE HOUSE

301-327 East Lawrence Avenue, Springfield, Illinois, U.S.A.

NATCHEZ PLANTATION HOUSE

735 North Atlantic Boulevard, Fort Lauderdale, Florida, U.S.A.

First Printing, 1969

Second Printing, 1971

With THOMAS BOOKS *careful attention is given to all details of
manufacturing and design. It is the Publisher's desire to present books
that are satisfactory as to their physical qualities and artistic possibilities
and appropriate for their particular use.* THOMAS BOOKS *will be true
to those laws of quality that assure a good name and good will.*

Printed in the United States of America

PP-22

PREFACE

The viewpoint and data supporting this work have emerged from approximately twenty-five years of very practical work in leading and supervising physical conditioning programs for men and women. Many types of programs have been tried out, usually over five to six months' duration, within the span of a single school year. Many experiments have been conducted by my graduate students, under my stimulation and supervision. There are approximately 150 graduate theses in this area at the University of Illinois, indexed and summarized in abstract form in the series of *Abstracts of Graduate Theses,* compiled and edited by me, over the past fifteen years. This work is very much a collation of these theses, supplemented by some of my own, and with my own version of their meanings.

Since this work is from the area of physical and health education, it has limitations. All tests are on human subjects under practical participation conditions (field experiments), usually without dietary control. To obtain statistical significance under such conditions is difficult but even the more remarkable as greater relative changes are demanded of the subjects. The Physical Fitness Research Laboratory, under my supervision, has tested as many as ten thousand adult subjects, usually before and after a given course of physical exercise or sports participation. Changes are shown in terms of anthropometric, circulatory-respiratory, and motor tests, which are comprehensively documented in various other works as shown in the literature referred to. Changes are then treated by statistical methods for reliability.

While reliability is important in terms of precision of the testing, the *changes* for each group of subjects in hand, and each case therein, are of paramount importance, as well as are the interpretations to each case. The practical testing program has permitted higher levels of motivation and the testing of many subjects. Validation is against the physiological laboratory type tests, so that the physiological meaning may be known. But after the validation has been established to a reasonable extent, it is the function of physical education to work with larger groups of people and to motivate them to participate. Personal leadership is of top priority.

Reference is given to the many collaborators in the literature cited. Even so, it is the briefest kind of summary with principal emphasis upon the protective and developmental, rather than the treatment of disease. Tests which could be traumatic, or which could require hospitalization for participants, are usually omitted. Tests which can be handled by physical education personnel have been featured. The correlative developmental exercise programs are to be found in other works by the author such as in *Physical Fitness and Dynamic Health, Physical Fitness Workbook, Fun in the Water, Warfare Aquatics, The Healthy Life* (Life-Time) and several minor manuals in which his preferred types of workouts have been recorded.

While a great deal of energy-cost work has been done in our laboratory and also many detailed analyses of exercises, these are not the main emphases in this volume. To look back on twenty-five years of work with the physical conditioning of adult men, in which not a single man has been lost through sudden death or heart attack, to reflect on the principal types of changes detected of a physical or physiological nature, is a challenge. While a correlative volume could be written on the psychological changes, the emphasis given to this summary is practical and physiological.

THOMAS KIRK CURETON

ACKNOWLEDGMENTS

I wish to acknowledge the splendid editorial assistance of the staff of Charles C Thomas, Publisher, and to thank Dr. Bruno Balke, Professor Burleigh Don Franks, and Maurice Jetté for reading the manuscript. Citations from other works and illustrations therefrom have been acknowledged individually where they occur in the text. Mrs. Mary Lee Jewett has drawn most of the graphs throughout the book.

T.K.C.

CONTENTS

Page

Preface v
Acknowledgments vii

Chapter

I. PHYSIOLOGICAL OBJECTIVES OF THE PHYSICAL FITNESS PROGRAMS WITH
MIDDLE-AGED SUBJECTS 3

Physiological Objectives to Develop Positive Dynamic Health . . . 3

Types of Exercises and Programs Used to Improve Adult Fitness . . 4

Basic Physical Fitness Programs—Types of Exercises, Games, Sports
and Recreations 6

Effect of Exercise upon Chronic Ailments—Development of General
Resistance 8

Practical Effects Related to Life 15

II. PHYSIOLOGICAL EFFECTS OF EXERCISE, BROADLY SUMMARIZED . . . 19

Effects upon the Circulatory, Nervous, and Glandular Systems
Generally 19

III. EVIDENCE OF PHYSIOLOGICAL FAILURE (DETERIORATION) 24

Deterioration of Physical Fitness with Age and Disuse 24

IV. SPECIFIC EFFECTS OF PHYSICAL TRAINING UPON MIDDLE-AGED SUBJECTS . 33

Reduction of Total Peripheral Resistance and Arterial Volume
Rigidity 33

Shrinkage in Heart Size with Physical Training in Middle-aged Men . 41

Sympathetic versus Parasympatheticotonic Effects, and
Normalization 44

Use of Exercise to Reduce Fat, Cholesterol, Triglycerides,
Phospholipids 52

Parallel Effects upon the Circulatory-Respiratory and Metabolic
Systems 56

Various Effects of Group Training Programs 62

Various Effects of Individualized Training Programs 77

Appendices   *Page*

A. PROGRESSIVE PULSE RATIO TEST AS AN INDICATOR OF OXYGEN SHORTAGE
    (OR EXERCISE TOLERANCE) AND PREDICTOR OF OXYGEN AVAILABIL-
    ITY FOR PROGRESSIVELY HARDER WORK INCREMENTS 90

    Validity of Various Submaximal Tests to Predict Performance . . . 95

    Cureton's Specifications for Progressive Pulse Ratio Test
        (Steps or Squats) 101

B. VALIDITY OF TESTING CARDIOVASCULAR FITNESS BY THE SPHYGMOGRAPH
    (EXTERNAL CUFF, HEARTOGRAPH) METHOD WITH THE CAMERON AND
    RELATED METHODS 118

C. OXYGEN INTAKE, DEFICIT (DEBT), AND ANOXIA PHOTOMETER TESTS . . 192

    Index 209

THE PHYSIOLOGICAL EFFECTS OF EXERCISE PROGRAMS ON ADULTS

I

PHYSIOLOGICAL OBJECTIVES OF THE PHYSICAL FITNESS PROGRAMS WITH MIDDLE-AGED SUBJECTS

PHYSIOLOGICAL OBJECTIVES TO DEVELOP POSITIVE DYNAMIC HEALTH

Physiological Objectives to Develop Vigor and Prevent Physical Deterioration

Evaluation of the various programs used in the adult physical fitness work leads to certain definite physiological objectives,[1,2] which may be listed as follows:

1. To develop more human energy to meet needs, and to remove aversion to physical work and vigorous participation in sports, exercises, and outdoor living.

2. To protect the human organism against sudden trauma, which may result from suddenly imposed stress, either physical or emotional.

3. To provide for gradual physiological warm-up but more and more total calories of work as time goes along with the physical training program (i.e. *Progression*).

4. To provide hygienic training experiences which, if pursued sufficiently long and hard enough, will serve to check or reverse the well-known tendencies toward physical deterioration which curves turn downhill in average Americans with ages spanning in the 25 to 30 years.

5. To develop the primary components of balance, flexibility, agility, strength, power, and endurance, so that higher and higher scores may be made on appropriate age tables, leading to an individual being better than average for chronological age.

6. To improve the cardiovascular-respiratory-metabolic functions, as represented in specific tests and performances such as certain endurance events which reflect these physiological parameters.

7. To strengthen and also balance the autonomic nervous system to resist stress under work conditions and to induce relaxation at rest. The possibility of exercise "normalizing" blood pressure, turning

up the depressive, anxious, low metabolism types (parasympatheti-
cally dominated), and relaxing the high-strung, hyperreactive, un-
economical types (sympathetically dominated) is real.

8. To reduce the total peripheral resistance and thus unburden the
heart from excessive overaction, and to normalize heart size.

9. To tune up the neuromuscular system for developing higher relative
strength per pound of body weight, faster total body reactions,
faster vision, and greater power.

10. To improve the glandular functioning (glands of the central glandular axis: pituitary, thyroid, pancreas, adrenals, and gonads).

11. To protect the middle-aged against premature heart disease, low
energy capacity, and premature failure in all aspects of physiological
functioning (nervous, circulatory, respiratory, digestive, eliminatory,
sexual, and volitional).

12. To strengthen the motivation, confidence, willpower, and integration capacity for physical performance and physiological function
by means of education, testing and rating (on scales and profiles).

13. To develop knowledge and insight into the various patterns of training to fit various needs.

14. To avoid overtraining and trauma by forewarnings and a casual
beginning (preseasoning) to any hard work.

15. To intersperse several weeks of training with at least one day each
week of genuine recreational activity (i.e. a game, hike, picnic, camp-
out, or dance).

TYPES OF EXERCISES AND PROGRAMS USED TO IMPROVE
ADULT FITNESS

Exercise—The Major Concern of Physical Educators

Exercise includes calisthenics (directed movements), games and sports,
recreation, and various types of physical work, as selected for study or to
be used in physical fitness tests. The calorie cost of many types of work
is known, also of many selected exercises. Somewhat less is known of the
energy cost of various games and sports, but this is rapidly being studied.

Because "exercise" is so poorly understood, it is necessary to take a
brief look at the many things which can be called exercise. Sports are
seldom continuous, like cross-country, riding (cycling), or rowing; they
are intermittent, providing for rest periods of various lengths and frequencies. The calorific cost of exercise may be all important if the total
of calories burned to reduce weight, fat, cholesterol, triglycerides, lipo-
proteins, and so forth is evaluated. Strength exercise usually involves using

relatively high resistance; power means using high speed; and balance features equilibrium and the. length of time it can be held.

Endurance may mean holding the performance continuous for at least a minute, but full warm-up may take as long as 20 to 40 minutes. Cross-country, as in running, swimming, sledding, cycling, skiing, or snowshoeing, means longer distance than a short sprint. Attempts have been made to get exercises of different types (balance, flexibility, agility, strength, power —and also some complicated coordinations) into a short time event, like the obstacle courses. Some patterns combine weight lifting or hard strength-endurance exercises with running a certain distance, usually called a circuit. Others are standardized distance-running courses with hurdles or obstacles intermittently spaced, known as steeplechases; and others are just lifting barbells or dumbbells in a prescribed number of repetitions. Pulleys, rowing machines, treadmills, and gadgets abound on every hand, but the effects produced are seldom evaluated, so understanding is in its infancy.

Two Principal Approaches to Health—Two Sides to the Coin

The traditional medical approach to good health is to conquer all infections and to eradicate disease germs. The other side of the coin, which appears to the writer to be just as important, is to create more human energy and resistance to fatigue and trauma through gradual progressive physical conditioning. To understand the potential of this, which may be as important as all other approaches put together, is to evaluate the effects of various physical activities from every point of view possible, but especially from the viewpoint of their effects upon fitness and health, both physical and mental.

It is a thesis that the cultivation of physical fitness, along with an optimum rhythm of life, leads to appreciably higher energy, better control of the body and relative freedom from handicapping strains, lethargy, and chronic ailments. Physical training leads to improved resistance to environmental stresses and most probably to similar resistance to emotional stresses as well. Physical fitness infers the opposite of being beset with infirmity, chronic ailments (viruses, weaknesses and fatigue). The demands of vigorous recreational living are well known, and not to be fit may exact a great penalty. But what this means in terms of the physiology of physical fitness needs to be spelled out. No one can do this with great finality at this time, but certain things are known and can be stated. The programs cannot be spelled out in full because of space limitations, but certain cross references can be made to correlative materials.[1, 2]

BASIC PHYSICAL FITNESS PROGRAMS—TYPES OF EXERCISES, GAMES, SPORTS, RECREATIONS

Most of our subjects do not know how to exercise when they first come to us. The introductory work is done by copying a leader, but at one's own pace at the start of the work. Newcomers are admonished to "learn the exercise properly but do not try to keep up with the leader if he goes too hard or too fast." The basic exercises are similar to those published in *Sports Illustrated* (Jan. 17, 1955).[3]

When the exercise is in the swimming pool, men are warmed up first with 25 minutes of continuous calisthenics, then sent to the showers to wash. Finally, they do the prescribed swimming program under supervision. Endurance is stressed. Every day, some part of the work is selected to be explained in a short talk, or in two or three short talks during recuperation "breaks" of 1 or 2 minutes while participants are walking or doing some light exercise.

Several patterns of endurance training are introduced in our program:
Rhythmical Endurance Exercises with Forced Breathing.
Walking or Swimming or Cycling, Hopping, Skipping.
Alternate Walking and Jogging, Bench Stepping.
Alternate Running-in-place with Various Other Endurance Exercises.
Following Cureton's *low gear system,* compare *Physical Fitness and Dynamic Health,* 1965.
Test Exercises of Balance, Flexibility, Agility, Strength, Power, and Endurance.

These patterns are sometimes imitative of the best training patterns known in athletics, but with the dosage cut down for interval training, Fartlek training, steeplechase, or obstacle courses.

In the basic program, daily attendance is carefully checked for all men being followed by tests, in matched groups, or on dietary supplement programs. Regularity is preached, day in and day out—also the gospel of "Make it up if you miss."

The basic program includes about 2 months for medical and dental exams, walking, tests, consultations, and prescriptions, four months of progressive exercise, and then almost 2 months of finishing off tests and measurements. Usually all areas are covered, involving about sixty tests. If the subject is very special, and the need is great enough, we may complete as many as 128 tests and measurements. One program is for women, another is for men. In a typical year we handle 150 to 300 middle-aged men, 30 to 60 women, 60 to 100 young men, and 75 to 100 boys in the basic program, not counting advanced special subjects such as athletes and certain control subjects who do not take the exercises. The progressive exercises are from *Physical Fitness and Dynamic Health.*[4]

Low Gear Work (Two to Six Months)

Warm-up consists of 15 to 20 minutes of forced breathing, rhythmic exercises for every part of the body stressing flexibility, rhythm and very moderate endurance. There is usually an alternation of easy work and slightly harder work. A hard exercise is always followed by a period of forced breathing, stretching, and easier work. Emphasis is upon gradual progression, such as walking at half-speed, race-walk, and then jog. Each exercise is begun slowly with full breathing. While all parts of the body are worked out, there is an avoidance of severe power exercises (speed) and very hard strength exercises which last longer than 10 to 15 seconds. Usually, the workout is about 30 minutes to begin, is extended to 40 minutes, and then to 50. All components are touched (balance, flexibility, agility, strength, power and endurance). Easiest tests are taken interspersed within the workout with some warm-up before the testing.

Middle Gear Work (One to Three Years)

Warm-up consists of 15 to 20 minutes of forced breathing and rhythmic endurance exercises for every part of the body. Various forms of interval training work (harder, then lighter; harder, then lighter) are used. All components are worked on as before but somewhat harder. The duration of each single exercise should be extended. Some breath holding for moderate periods is introduced. Longer and longer work is done in walking, jogging, running (or swimming, skating, skiing, climbing, camping, canoeing, rowing, etc.). Intermediate tests are taken. "Push-for-the-peak" is used but with intermediate efforts.

Wind sprints (repetitious bursts).

Long walks, hikes, swims, cycling trips, runs (as in cross-country).

Weekend camping, hiking, climbing, canoeing, cycling, rowing.

Take all tests, record performances.

High Gear Work (Once or Twice Weekly, or Four to Eight Weeks Every Second Day)

Warm up 30 minutes with forced breathing and more severe testing to the virtual all-out level, provided the previous *low gear* and *middle gear* build-up work is done in a gradual build-up sequence. More use is made of test exercises, or competition. Longer and longer work is completed at faster and faster pace, with one real test of endurance each time the workout occurs. Five or six near-all-out events are used involving different muscles:

Double dose, triple dose, quadruple dose.

Hard tests for time or endurance.

Steeplechase work; obstacle courses, work for better time and endurance.

Energy Cost Evaluation

The energy cost evaluation of the *low, middle, high* programs in Cureton's Progressive Program have been evaluated by Cureton and Kapilian[5] at the Physical Fitness Research Laboratory, University of Illinois. For various subjects, the kilocalorie cost is 100 to 200 kilocalories for the *low gear,* 300 to 500 kilocalories for the *middle gear,* and 600 to 1000 kilocalories for the *high gear,* depending upon the weight of the subject and the pace at which he can go, progressing from 30 minutes to 40 to 50 minutes.

EFFECT OF EXERCISE UPON CHRONIC AILMENTS— DEVELOPMENT OF GENERAL RESISTANCE

There is a great deal of testimony that gradual and progressive physical training, in a wave-like rhythm, produces a *general resistance;* if and when the training is too hard, in too short a time to adapt, there may be a lowering of specific resistance.[6, 7] It is generally true that groups of men in regular training, as observed for instance in the YMCA Adult Fitness Programs, report fewer chronic complaints on checklists. In many hundreds of interviews and testimonial letters, which cannot be reproduced here, a persistent testimony bears out that there is a gradual overcoming of such complaints as digestive upsets, heartburn, acidosis, diabetic tendency, constipation, headaches, fat, fatigue, hemorrhoids, sex dysfunction, heart thumping (emotional excitability), chest pain, abdominal pain, painful feet, eye watering (weakness), sinusitis, swollen joints (Table I). The causes of such ailments are stress and lack of movement.

Swollen joints may be due to poor circulation but also occasionally to infection in some part of the body, such as in the prostate or at the root of a tooth. It is best to have a medical checkup when such troubles appear. A swollen knee, for instance, due to excessive overbending of the knee, may be gradually reduced by riding a bicycle with gradual increase of the resistance, either naturally or artificially, or sometimes by work on a rowing machine, while excessive bending is eliminated.

Fatigue is associated with lowered cardiovascular-respiratory tests, with low basal metabolism, and with long-continued emotional excitement. There may also be psychological depressions with extremely slow pulse rates and low blood pressures. Excessively low or high blood pressures usually do respond to regular, moderate endurance work but may become worse after sudden, violent exertions to which the subject does not adapt. Poor circulation may cause an anoxic pain in some part of the body, as when a shoe is too tight and there is long inactivity. Just to walk on the foot without unloosing the lace will usually result in the pain going

TABLE I

HEALTH COMPLAINTS OF ADULT MALES (26 to 60 Yrs)

	Champaign-Urbana Men (General Sample)		Other Men in Training (YMCA Men in Active Program)	
	N	%	N	%
Digestive upset	19	19.0	23	16.79
Heartburn	14	14.0	17	12.41
Acidosis	10	10.0	11	8.03
Diabetes	2	2.0	1	.73
Constipation	13	13.0	13	9.49
Headaches	22	22.0	15	10.95
Fat	12	12.0	8	5.84
Fatigue (morning)	14	14.0	5	3.65
Fatigue (noon)	11	11.0	7	5.11
Fatigue (night)	38	38.0	15	10.95
Hemorrhoids	17	17.0	7	5.11
Sex Dysfunction	1	1.0	0	0
Heart thump	4	4.0	4	2.92
Chest pain	3	3.0	1	1.73
Abdominal pain	3	3.0	8	5.84
Painful feet	12	12.0	10	7.30
Eye trouble	21	21.0	15	10.95
Sinusitis	20	20.0	14	10.22
Swollen joints	2	2.0	1	1.73
	N = 100		N = 137	

$r = .67$
(Rank Order)
Correlation

Note: Results in TABLE I sum up to less digestive trouble, less constipation, and less fat, as well as to half the number of headaches, half as many complaints about eyes and chronic sinusitis, and to only a third as many complaints of fatigue and hemorrhoids.

away. Improved circulation results in reduction of the swelling. Abnormally high pulse rates may reflect fatigue, lack of economy, or some maladjustment reflected in the stress effect. It may be, too, that there is a bacterial or virus infection at work placing stress on the body.

Jack J. Joseph in his article entitled The Relationship of Selected Fitness Test Scores to the Chronic Complaints and Ailments of Adult Males (*J Sport Med*, 7:83-94, June 1967), has made an extensive analysis of the chronic complaints and ailments of adult males as related to the test scores on a variety of physical fitness tests, using Cureton's checklists and also his tests as used in the eight-station Battery, in his YMCA Clinics, and in the Physical Fitness Research Laboratory. After Cureton introduced these into the Seattle YMCA in 1960, 110 adult males (22 to 67 yrs, avg. of 41.18 yrs) were interviewed and tested. About one third of the men suffered from chronic fatigue and tension, and a lesser percentage complained of joint trouble, sinusitis, nasal trouble, heart palpitation, excess fat, low backaches, high blood pressure, painful feet, and gastrointestinal troubles. These same men rated low in heart rate and blood pressure reactions to bench stepping; they had poor strength, flexibility, and balance; and they were typically overweight and had depressed brachial pulse waves. Joseph reports that after several months of physical-fitness work, following the outlines of the Cureton Progressive, Rhythmic Endurance Exercise System, many of the complaints and inhibitions were eliminated. Nearly all of the men studied were desk-bound college graduates. Incidence percentage corresponded closely to Cureton's own report on one hundred men (Table I).

Intercorrelations are reported on the thirty-three physical fitness tests used in the Cureton Physical Fitness Clinics, and means and standard deviations are given, along with age, height, and weight.

		Percent			Percent
1.	Fatigue before noon time	51.82	9.	Digestive upsets	13.64
2.	Pinched-up fat greater		10.	Sinusitis	12.73
	than 1 inch	43.64	11.	Joint trouble	11.82
3.	Nervous tension	37.38	12.	Headaches	9.09
4.	Low backache	29.09	13.	Chest pain	7.27
5.	Cigarette smoking	28.18	14.	Heart thumping	6.36
6.	Nasal trouble	20.0	15.	High blood pressure	5.45
7.	Eye trouble	19.09	16.	Foot trouble	2.73
8.	Restless sleep	19.09	17.	Diabetes	1.82

The objective measurements reported by Joseph closely resembled Cureton's data on middle-aged males (26 to 60 yrs) in body measurements, flexibility, strength, and motor performance. The cardiovascular responses were slightly poorer (Fig. 1).

The five measurements taken from the heartograph indicated typically untrained cardiovascular systems, in that the subjects typically exhibited characteristics of "loafer's heart" (*cf.* Appendix B):

1. Low stroke volume (by area under the brachial pulse wave).
2. Retarded rebound in the brachial artery (diastolic amplitude).
3. Weak ejection amplitude.
4. Slower velocity of ejection (by obliquity angle).
5. Fast heart rate.

A varimax factor analysis of fifty-three variables, combining the objective fitness tests and the chronic ailments, produced twelve factors:

FIGURE 1. Chronic complaints of 100 middle-aged males, ages 26 to 67. (From Cureton, T. K.: *Physical Fitness Appraisal and Guidance*. St. Louis, Mosby, 1947, p. 485.)

		Total Variance (%)
1.	Lack of vagus tone	19.66
2.	Brachial pulse wave amplitude	12.13
3.	Static dynamometer strength	9.27
4.	Body size (fat)	9.27
5.	Dynamic strength	7.44
6.	Strength/weight and power and digestive upsets	7.12
7.	Nervous exhaustion (fatigue, tension, and diabetes)	5.98
8.	Rigidity (chest pain, age and lack of trunk-forward flexibility)	5.46
9.	Back and shoulder extension flexibility	6.76
10.	Effect of tobacco, headaches and digestive upsets	5.64
11.	Respiratory deficiency, nasal trouble	5.54
12.	Cardiovascular adjustment to exercise	5.71

This study is wholly cross-sectional, and no longitudinal parallel effects could possibly be traced. Casual analysis cannot be inferred from factor analysis, and no real effects of an ongoing exercise program could be determined. The chronic complaints, as checked by the men at a single sitting, do not have a high relationship to the objective tests given. A longitudinal study of the correlative changes might yield a higher association.

The Integration Effect, Resistance to Stress

There are at least three principal effects which may be considered *general* because they are usually felt throughout the body and are not specifically in one part of the body i.e. in the toe, eye, stomach, hand, etc. Generalized effects are apt to be regulated mainly by effects upon the nervous system, and sometimes by the nervous system affecting the circulatory system, and possibly by the nervous system affecting the digestive or glandular system. Most of all, it would be wrong to visualize the effects of exercise as mainly making a larger biceps muscle or larger calf.

There are well-established concepts that the several systems of the body work in physiological cooperation (synergism). Fritz Kahn[8] states,

> Although we still discuss the body in terms of various systems, we are thus more than ever aware that all systems are interconnected and interdependent. We are aware too, how that seemingly incorporeal system, the mind, influences all of the other systems, and conversely, how the body, especially in accident and illness, affects one's state of mind. Modern medicine, especially in the fields of psychiatry and psychosomatics, has driven home the point that glands and emotions, nerves and digestion, mental states and blood pressure and heart condition, are indivisible—fused with inconceivable subtlety and complexity into a single wonderful organism—the human body.

As an example of such integration, studies of motor-nerve conduction velocities have been made in the median, ulnar, radial, peroneal and tibial nerves, comparing patients suffering from renal insufficiency with normal subjects.[9] A statistically significant slowing of nervous conduction velocity was noted in such patients. It may be hard to say which condition caused which, but probably there is reciprocal interaction. Such associations are very important because various conditions of malfunctioning are reflected in the nervous system and vice versa.[10, 11] The organismic effect, long-recognized in psychology,[12] has a realism in human physiology in relationship to stress effects, as Selye and others have pointed out. The exercise of humans usually involves the *total* body approach, first by means of physical performance and physique tests, and then may be supplemented by further tests (hematological, metabolic, and psychological).

Selye's Principles

Over the years, Hans Selye of Montreal has completed extensive documentation to show that the *adaptation syndrome* is a basic proposition for man facing stress.[13-16] The stages of (1) *alarm*, (2) *resistance* (adaptation), and (3) *over stress, collapse,* and *possible death* are all well recognized. It happens that in the human exercise work there is almost never death, and the human sequence is perhaps better described in five stages: (1) *alarm* (marked sympathetic excitement), (2) *resistance* (adjustment to the stress), (3) *trained homeodynamics* (holding the trained state without harm), (4) *overtraining* (temporary exhaustion but not death), and (5) *possibility of death* (seldom seen).

A great deal of evidence does exist which pertains to the reversal of the trends of deterioration. To the extent that measures of strength, agility, endurance, and other major traits are improved as the direct result of training programs, then such margins of improvement as are shown *are not due to heredity.* Selye's hypothesis holds that the development of *general resistance* depends upon adequate stimulation of the hypophysis-adrenal system and the secretion of adrenocorticotropic hormones and glucocorticoids in *adequate* amount. There is also a rise in osmotic resistance, along with other tissue changes, particularly the persistence of the nervous stimulation (a type of memory). The ability of the brain, spinal cord, and sensory nervous system to resist pain, exertion, and temperature—and the stimulation of the glandular system (adrenals, thryroid, sex, etc.)—seems very important since deterioration of these glands is associated with physical debility. In people who become progressively unfit, there is also progressive concomitant loss of ability to withstand stress. Physical training is probably the best way to train the body and the mind to resist stress, and thus to retain youthfulness and athletic ability. Some of the human training experiments in Cureton's own series on humans seem to provide impressive evidence of the benefits of progressive physical training.[17-22]

What Selye emphasizes now, after many years of work in the area

of "prestress" training as applied to exercise, is the principle that preliminary training of a moderate sort before a severe bout and staying
fit enough to bear a sudden stress will prevent the sometimes disastrous
trauma. This principle which Selye explains is essentially the same principle which underlies the *low, middle,* to *high* gear progression so widely
applied now in progressive physical training programs.

It is *not* implied that physical exercise will prevent or cure all disease,
as nothing could be so erroneous as such a statement. But in the areas
of buffering stress and strengthening a person to bear stress of many
kinds, exercise is very important. Zimkin and Korobkov[23] have documented
various studies to show that systematic physical training makes one more
efficient, so that the same work can be done on less and less oxygen, or
under hard (maximal) exertion more and more oxygen is made available,
through conditioning of the nervous and circulatory-respiratory systems.
Animal research has also shown improved resistance to cold, heat, and
radiation. Resistance is both *general* and *specific.*

It is now claimed that the use of an anti-inflammatory diet and the
systematic training of the thermoregulatory system have some value in
preventing respiratory and throat infections in persons undergoing training
programs.[24] Similarly, the use of the fortified diet, daily supplement of
an all-around vitamin capsule, along with additional amounts of vitamin
B.complex and vitamin C plus wheat germ and wheat germ oil, is now
in common use in programs of hard athletic stress.[25]

Mateef[26] takes the position that exercise (physical training) is a process
of complex nervous excitation, and the neuromuscular system in turn brings
about an overloading of the cardiovascular system by pumping the blood
through the blood vessels (veins)—blood which the heart then ejects. The
system is weak unless there is muscular tone and a good deal of movement.
The movement involves the brain, the circulatory-respiratory systems, the
glandular and excretory systems, and the metabolism of the body as a
whole. Mateef[27] has reviewed the evidence that continuous functional
activity of the body and mind through physical activity preserves the
brain and the body, too. But, he points out, the struggle to preserve the
human organism should begin early, and not after advanced senescence
has set in. Wittich[28] points out that functional impairment leads to
neurosis and emphasizes that compartmentalized treatment—whether phar-
macological, psychological, or physiotherapeutic—fails to take account of
the multifactorial interdependence of the phenomena.

But there are indications that the development of *general resistance,*
improved circulation, and better respiration are basic to health. Dentists
discovered, in comparing persistently exercised rats, that for about three
quarters of their estimated life span (for 4 hrs per day) with sedentary

rats kept in cages, the exercised rats (61) developed 4.3 caries per animal and the confined rats (192) developed 14.0 caries per animal.[29]

Beyond a doubt, persistent exercise over long enough time tends to minimize or obliterate chronic ailments, but much more work needs to be done to spell out these relationships more exactly.[30]

PRACTICAL EFFECTS RELATED TO LIFE

Most marvelous and practical of all, from the point of view of doing work, is the relatively great improvement in muscular endurance, due partially to improving the cardiovascular condition and also to specific conditioning of the muscle-nerve junctions and neural pathways of control. Coordination, speed, and resistance against fatigue increase, as well as does strength. Such changes are to be considered mainly as changes in the nervous system. Strength per pound of body weight increases in the force and speed exercises of the power type, although mesomorphs will usually be found to have the best scores if they are in ordinary condition. Even mesomorphs deteriorate greatly if they give up all exercise. Strength is important; strength is required to move the body about continuously in walking, running, swimming, climbing, hiking with a load, chopping wood, paddling a canoe, pedalling a bicycle uphill, and in doing all kindred activities which make us useful and practical in life.

The trained man or woman usually looks better after training than when untrained. The posture will usually be better, or there will be relatively better circulation in the same postures. We all know the firm, healthy look about the face of the athlete. The expanded chest, relative to the size of the normal abdominal girth, will be greater than in the untrained person. While for athletic advantage a wide shoulder breadth related to the width of the hips is preferred, we see that there are many different types of activities in sport, and there is literally a place for every type of physique. The expert will understand these relationships so that guidance can be given to the many who do not understand their natural aptitudes. The "lateral" type of physique will always be broader than the "linear" type, despite any plan or pattern of exercise, but it is possible to slim or thicken the body within reasonable limits if the right pattern of exercise is followed with great enough intensity. The evidence of the effects of exercise upon physique has been reviewed.[31-35].

It is very impressive to see how young men and elderly men, and even housewives, improve under the influences of physical training. Such changes are usually from 30 to 50 standard score per cent following intensive training programs in the motor fitness tests, which indicate degrees of ability in balance, flexibility, agility, strength, power, and endurance. Studies of these changes have shown, however, that there are many specific types of effects. I am prompted to say that a man is very nearly what his activity or his lack of activity makes him. It is humbly suggested that we spend more time studying these types of changes rather than preaching that exercise is harmful unless wisely directed. We do not appreciate the oft repeated phrase, "endurance exercises will hurt young children," when no data are given to support the statement. I would say that any activity is better than no activity. The aim of medicine and physical education alike is to understand the effects of various types of exercises, and we have hardly begun to examine the evidence for the integrating effect of exercise. Many of the benefits which we value highly do not seem to occur under casual group game participation but require gradual progressive forms of training which finally reach harder levels of work than is usually provided in volleyball, bowling, golf, and social games.

In modern civilization we have an enormous amount of sitting and static standing in the white collar office work, in the factories, and in the social diversions which involve eating, drinking, gambling, playing cards, lounging in clubs and at teas and receptions. If one wants to avoid fattening arteries, flaccid vessels and muscular tissue, paunches and ptoses, he will keep on the move more; he will exercise more and cultivate a willingness to do physical work. It certainly seems true that people lose their circulatory fitness because of too little activity and too much alcohol and fried food. In the examination of several thousands of middle-aged men, we have found that the ones who have good circulatory fitness are those who have kept up their activity and eat and drink very moderately. Those who deteriorate relatively quickly seem to be muscular men who have gone sedentary—those who have grown soft and fat from exercise only with their tongues, eyes, and pencils. The emphasis of the medical, religious, and educational professions upon passive procedures which bring indoor confinement have placed a social emphasis upon sedentary pursuits to the detriment of health. Some individuals within these groups have even decried the values of exercise to health, and they point to great athletes who have deteriorated. We have the beginnings of understanding in this area but, as an area of applied science which deserves development, we have a long way to go with the experimental work. It is quite probable that the fountain of youth for middle-aged people will be found in the wise use of leisure time to maintain their physical fitness. With the development of more places like the Physical Fitness Research Centers comes the possibility of guiding businesses, industries, and individuals by means of good examinations and the prescription of positive health-building procedures, and by the demonstration of good exercises and fitness procedures.

References

1. CURETON, T. K.: Physical fitness work with normal aging adults, *J Phys Ment Rehab, 11*:145-149, Sept.-Oct. 1957.
2. CURETON, T. K.: Basic principles of physical fitness work for adults, *J Phys Ed* (YMCA), *41*:51, Jan.-Feb. 1944.
3. WHITE, WM. H.: Exercises to keep fit, *Sports Illustrated, 2*:63-65, Jan. 17, 1955.
4. CURETON, T. K.: *Physical Fitness and Dynamic Health*, New York, Dial, 1965.
5. KAPILIAN, RALPH H.: Progressive Exercises for Adults Using Various Cardiovascular Indices in Determining the Exertion of these Exercises. M. S. Thesis, Physical Education, U. of Ill., 1961.
6. SELYE, HANS: The role of stress in the production and prevention of experimental cardiopathies. In Raab, Wilhelm (Ed.): *Prevention of Ischemic Heart Disease*. Springfield, Thomas, 1966, pp. 163-168.
7. ZIMKIN, N. V., and KOROBKOV, A. Y.: The importance of physical exercise as a factor of increasing the resistance of the body to unfavorable influence under conditions of modern civilization. *XVI Weltkongress fur Sportmedicin*, Hannover, 1966, pp. 63-70.
8. KAHN, FRITZ: Foreword. In *The Human Body*. New York, Random, 1965.
9. HONET, J. C.; JEBSEN, R. H., and TENCKHOFF, H. A.: Motor nerve condition velocity in chronic renal insufficiency. *Arch Phys Med, 47*:647-652, Oct. 1966.
10. JOHNSON, E. W., and OLSEN, K. J.: Clinical value of motor nerve conduction velocity determinations. *JAMA, 17*:2030-2035, April 30, 1960.
11. NORRIS, A. H.; SHOCK, N. W., and WAGNER, I. H.: Age changes in the maximum conduction velocity of motor fibers of human ulnar nerves. *J Appl Physiol, 5*:589-593, April, 1953.
12. GUTIN, R.: Organismic interaction: Implications for physical education research. *Res Quart, 37*:562-563, Dec. 1966.
13. SELYE, HANS: *Stress*, Montreal, Acta, Inc., 1950. (822 pages, plus 203 pages of references.)
14. SELYE, HANS: *1st Annual Report on Stress*, Montreal, Acta, Inc., 1951. (511 pages, plus 153 pages of bibliography.)
15. SELYE, HANS: *The Story of the Adaptation Syndrome*, Montreal, Acta, Inc., 1952.
16. SELYE, HANS: *The Stress of Life*, New York, McGraw, 1956.
17. CURETON, T. K.: Physical fitness improvement of a middle-aged man, with brief reviews of related studies. *Res Quart, 23*:149-160, May 1952.
18. CURETON, T. K., and POHNDORF, R. H.: Influence of wheat germ oil as a dietary supplement in a program of conditioning exercises with middle-aged subjects. *Res Quart, 26*:391-407, Dec. 1955.
19. CURETON, T. K.; SMILEY, W. A.; GANSLEN, R.; SUSIC, S., and WHITE, C.: Effect of physical training and a wheat germ oil dietary supplement upon the T-wave of the EGG and the Bicycle Ergometer Endurance Test. *Med Sport (Roma), 13*:490-505, Oct. 1959.
20. CURETON, T. K.: Physical training helps to regulate and improve glandular functions. *Res Quart, 30*:266-284, Oct. 1959.
21. CURETON, T. K.: Physical fitness changes in middle-aged men attributable to equal

eight-weeks periods of training, non-training and re-training. *J Sport Med,* 2:87-93, Nov.-Dec. 1962.

22. CURETON, T. K.: Improvements in physical fitness associated with a course of U.S. Navy underwater trainees, with and without dietary supplements. *Res Quart,* 34:440-453, Dec. 1963.

23. ZIMKIN and KOROBKOV, *op. cit.*

24. WORLD HEALTH ORGANIZATION: Nutrition and infection, Report No. 25, Expert Committee on Nutrition, Geneva. Joint FAO/WHO Committee, 1962, p. 19.

25. CURETON, T. K.: New training methods and dietary supplements are responsible for many of the new records. *Athletic J,* 42:12-14+, Jan. 1962.

26. MATEEF, D.: The new in the theory of exercise and it's influence on growth, development and aging. *XVI Weltkongress Für Sportmedicin,* Hannover, 1966, pp. 379-383.

27. MATEEF, D.: Morphological and physiological factors of aging and longevity. *Health and Fitness in the Modern World* (Rome Conference). Chicago, Athletic Institute, 1961, pp. 3-7.

28. WITTICH, G. H.: Functional impairment and neuroses. *XVI Weltkongress Für Sportmedicin,* Hannover. 1966, pp. 425-428.

29. STEINMAN, R. R.; BRASSETT, M., and TARTARYN, P.: Comparison of caries incidence in exercised and in immobilized rats. *J Dent Res,* 90:218, Jan.-Feb. 1961.

30. FRANK, K.: The strengthening of defenses against infection in high-performance athletes. *XVI Weltkongress Für Sportmedicin,* Hannover, 1966, pp. 221-225.

31. CURETON, T. K.: The effects of physical training, sports, and exercise on weight, fat and tissue proportions. *Professional Contributions.* Washington, *Amer Acad Phys Educ,* Nov. 1958.

32. CURETON, T. K.: The training and seasoning of muscles, tendons and ligaments, part 1. *J Phys Ment Rehab,* 16:80-85, May-June 1962; part II, pp. 103-106, July-August 1962.

33. CURETON, T. K., Chairman: In *Physical Fitness.* Washington, Research Monograph of the Amer Ass Health, Phys Educ and Rec, May 1941.

34. CURETON, T. K.: Effect of activities on external fat. In *Physical Fitness Appraisal and Guidance.* St. Louis, Mosby, 1947, pp. 156-157.

35. CURETON, T. K.: Anatomical, physiological and psychological changes induced by exercise programs in adults. In *Exercise and Fitness.* Chicago, Athletic Institute, 1960.

II

PHYSIOLOGICAL EFFECTS OF EXERCISE, BROADLY SUMMARIZED

EFFECTS UPON THE CIRCULATORY, NERVOUS, AND GLANDULAR SYSTEMS—GENERALLY

In the trained state, the nervous system is prepared for action rather than "inaction." In general, the individual is trained away from persistent sedentary tendencies and toward higher sympathetic *and* vagus tone. The heart becomes more capable of quick acceleration and longer rest. Training improves the blood flow persistently and improves cardiovascular tests of several types: (1) the Blood Flow Tests, (2) the Autonomic Balance, and (3) the Hydrostatic Adjustment Tests. Low cardiovascular test scores indicate that the cardiovascular system and the supporting nervous system are not trained for action or stamina and that there is relatively less resistance against the fatigue associated with blood stasis or peripheral vasoconstriction and other extreme tensive conditions, muscular or vascular.

In Geiger counter tests on five-hundred industrial workers, Dr. Hardin Jones* of the University of California discovered that the average 18-year-old has 25 cubic centimeters (cc) of blood passing through one liter of muscle. At age 25, this drops to 16 cc (40% less) and by 35 it is down to 10 cc (60% less). What does this prove? It proves that men—even young men—are not doing enough vigorous exercises to keep the blood flowing through the muscles—an important key to physical fitness. It proves that physiological aging comes upon modern man with astonishing rapidity, particularly the sedentary businessman who is probably tied to a desk from nine to five, and often longer.

Time is a most important factor in developing muscle tone, oxygen intake capacity, endurance, and better circulation. There are no effective "instant" programs.

Health, endurance, nutrition, and general well-being are all dependent upon a common denominator—*circulatory fitness.* The only way to gain this is by a systematic method of exercise. How much exercise can improve the circulation is more or less a mystery to most men, who may

---

*Time, Oct. 20, 1952, p. 85.

prefer weight training because they can see some effect in their muscles but not in the capillaries. Exercise opens up capillaries which are not otherwise open. Hormones from the adrenals also open them.

Why are these tiny vessels so important? The muscles, spinal cord, brain, lungs, nerves, and organs in general are penetrated by countless numbers of capillaries. The large arteries from the heart diminish in size until they are called arterioles; then these branch out and get smaller to become the capillaries. No matter how small, these smallest vessels are controlled by microscopic nerves which are called fibrils. Exercise affects these nerves and causes them to produce dilation in the vessels. Thus, the capillaries are not fixed in size but expand according to need. When we work up enough energy and heat by exercise they will expand so that more blood can be distributed throughout the body. But under tensions and various types of anxieties, or while smoking, these small vessels contract and the circulation is impaired.

As a man (or woman) gets older, youth gradually disappears in proportion to the ebbing of metabolism and circulation. To retain the physical capacities of youth, then, he must maintain his circulatory and muscular fitness. The fight is mainly to keep his capillaries open by constantly working the body. Otherwise, he will grow old prematurely, participate less in vigorous sports, and lose his physical courage to some extent. Forced to give up youthful pleasures, he will become more and more introverted with such tendencies as anxiety, oversensitiveness, overeating and overdrinking, mental fatigue, boredom, and lack of mental-physical integration.

Tests have shown that *all these traits are inversely related to the amount of time that he can run on a treadmill or do a similar endurance test.* Hence, endurance and circulation are tied up with personality. Obviously, from all that is known, there is an interplay (reciprocal interaction) between the nervous, circulatory, glandular, and excretory systems. Oxygen supply and nutrition undergird all continuous physical performance, and skill enters into every physical performance.

Actually, studies point to the fact that an athlete will maintain his circulatory fitness much longer if he continues to exercise throughout his life. This has been noted in some great world-class runners, such as Hannes Kohelemainen, Joie Ray, Lauri Pihkala, and Emil Zatopec. These men have demonstrated ability and endurance long after middle age. It is an obvious fact that endurance work continued into ripe old age is good for the heart. In fact, it is most probable that such exercise should never be given up at all.

Bodily movement trains the heart and increases circulation. In movement there is a nervous stimulation of the sympathetic branches of the autonomic nervous system. Lack of movement quickly leads to deterioration of the circulation. In fact, bed rest has been warned against very much recently in light of some of the findings showing progressive reduction of blood volume, joint stiffening, and deterioration of glandular functioning.[36, 37]

The heart is not a vacuum pump and cannot suck the blood up from the feet and legs to the heart when the body is in the upright position. But there are muscular movements, involuntary contractions stirred up reflexly, and wave pulsations which help the blood to lift itself against gravity. The role of the sympathetic nervous system is involved to stimulate the return circulation as well as the forceful ejection of the blood from the heart. But in long-continued sedentary life, there may be a progressive deterioration of the sympathetic vasodilator branches of the autonomic nervous system, and the synergic correlation of constriction and dilation fails, accompanied by progressive loss of circulation.

As body heat rises from exercise, more and more capillaries begin to function. Vigorous exercise also results in the pumping actions of the diaphragm and chest, which aspirate the blood upward into the thorax. Forced breathing has a value for this purpose. Forceful use of the lungs, alternated with breath holding, develops more oxygen intake capacity, probably because of the development of more capillaries and ventilatory capacity.

Exercise warm-up definitely increases the amount of blood going through the heart-lung circuit (and lung capillaries).[38] Continuous training serves to force more and more blood through the circuit, and the nerves become trained to open the circuit quickly. Such responsiveness will usually become lost with age unless one performs endurance work throughout the whole life. Few data exist on the training effects of very old people.

It is interesting to note that the speed of reactions to light and sound stimuli is increased by training. It is impressive that such improved responsiveness is reflected in other systems, even paralleling the improvement of plasma flow through the kidneys and basal metabolic rate. Speed of reaction improves somewhat with improved glandular functioning. Such reactions are not "fixed in the body type" nearly so much as they are the result of efficient use. In certain training experiments, the reaction times of the vertical jump have been improved by repetitious practice as much as fifty standard scores in a 6-month training program designed to do this.

Great nervous economy can result from physical training with respect to performing specific work tasks. But we must be aware that one specific work task is no measure of many other work tasks. We tested a top swimmer who was very efficient in the pool but who was not trained for running; he was very poor on the treadmill. In testing several men for maximal oxygen intake in the pool, on the bicycle and on the treadmill, the results were found quite variable for each individual, depending upon his coordination in each event. Lack of coordination causes a loss of economy, partly through "tensing up" and poor breathing, involving too many noncontributing muscles, and less oxygen intake than is needed. An example of high relative coordination was seen in our work with John Marshall, great Olympic swimmer who apparently knew how to relax and hold a fast rhythm better than most swimmers, and this was probably why he did relatively better.

The lungs may be thought of as a principal bottleneck if they are not conditioned by vigorous use, day by day. The dirty air, smoking or breathing smoke, and lack of vigorous pumping movements of the thorax, all may lead to serious deterioration. Forced breathing is now thought of as a good exercise in itself, but it should be done with exercise to avoid hyperventilation syndrome.

The use of the legs has been emphasized by Dr. Paul D. White; again and again has he hammered away at the need to understand this. It is one main key to good circulation, as is total immersion under water to add water pressure to the veins. When "bobbing" is performed in water 8 to 10 feet deep, the changing water pressure, along with the forceful use of the chest and lungs, greatly helps the circulation. Studies have shown that total circulation may increase about 25 per cent in a person just being quietly immersed under the surface of the water; swimming movements make more circulation; and bobbing up and down for considerable time with forced breathing is a vigorous circulatory-respiratory exercise.

The Training of Elderly Subjects

It has been demonstrated that subjects over 60 years of age may be progressively trained until they can not only take hard exercise but can make unusual performances compared with their peers. Remarkable improvements and unusually good performances were demonstrated by training such men as Joie Ray,[39] E. D. Walker,[40] and Syd Meadow.[41]. Barry has also demonstrated unusual improvements in men over sixty trained on bicycle ergometer work.[42, 43] Kraus and Raab[44] have set forth the thesis of *hypokinetic disease* in which they tell of many diseases caused by lack of exercise which are both neuromuscular and circulatory-respiratory in nature. Richard A. Asher[45] has made a comprehensive review of the diastrous effects of long periods in bed.

References

36. OLSON, EDITH V.: The hazards of immobility. *Amer J Nurs, 67*:780-797, April 1967.

37. ASHER, RICHARD A.: Dangers of going to bed. *Brit Med J, 2*:967-968, Dec. 13, 1947.

38. JOHNSON, R. L.; SPICER, W. S.; BISHOP, J. M., FORESTER, R. E.: Pulmonary capillary blood volume, flow and diffusing capacity. *J Appl Physiol, 15*:893, Sept. 1960.

39. CURETON, T. K.: A physical fitness case study of Joie Ray (60 to 70 yrs.). *J Phys Ment Rehab, 18*:64-72+, May-June 1964.

40. CURETON, T. K.: A case study report of Professor E.D.W. (58 to 74 years). *J Phys Ment Rehab, 19*:144-148, Sept.-Oct. 1955.

41. CURETON, T. K.: A case study of Sydney Meadows. *J Phys Ment Rehab, 19*:36-43, March-April 1965.

42. BARRY, ALAN J.; DALY, J. W.; ESTHER PRUITT, D. R.; STEINMETZ, J. R.; PAGE, H. F.; BIRKHEAD, N. C., and RODAHL, KAARE: The effects of physical conditioning on older individuals. I. Work capacity, circulatory-respiratory function and work electrocardiogram. *J Geront, 21*:182-191, April 1966.

43. BARRY, ALAN J.; STEINMETZ, J. R.; PAGE, H. F., and RODAHL, KAARE: The effects of physical conditioning on older individuals. II. Motor performance and cognitive function. *J Geront, 21*:192-199, Apr. 1966.

44. KRAUS, HANS, and RAAB, WILHELM: Hypokinetic Disease (with Foreword by Dr. Paul D. White). Springfield, Thomas, 1961.

45. ASHER, RICHARD A., *op. cit.*

III

EVIDENCE OF PHYSIOLOGICAL FAILURE
(DETERIORATION)

DETERIORATION OF PHYSICAL FITNESS WITH AGE AND DISUSE

Deterioration of Motor Physiological Functions with Age and Disuse

The rapid loss of all principal basic motor abilities is clearly documented (Fig. 2). As an example, the deterioration curve of 2,200 adults is shown, the curve turning downward at 26 years of age, as reflected in the 18-Item Motor Fitness Test. This test has been given to many thousands of individuals all over the country, especially in the YMCA's adult physical fitness classes. While it has been published in various Cureton publications, it is dramatically illustrated in *The Healthy Life* by TIME-LIFE Special Projects' issue.[46] It has also been published in *Redbook*[47] and *Sports Illustrated*.[48] It was first published in the *Physical Fitness Workbook*.[49] Its high relationship to the Illinois 14-Item Test was also established.[50]

It is universally observed that people lose their physical abilities as they age. It is most probable that "disuse" is the greatest single factor in such deterioration. The real question is, of course, to what extent do the organic capacities (such as ability to think; to function sexually; to have good digestion and assimilation; to retain warm hands and feet; to keep in good function the sight, hearing, touch, taste, and sense of position—all of these including the circulatory-respiratory functions) fail parallel to the motor functions?

Anton Carlson, eminent human biologist, ascribed to the human brain the most tenacity to hold on to function. Yet many people fail prematurely: some six-hundred thousand are in hospitals because of mental failure, and at least twenty million more suffer transient losses which, if indefinitely continued, destroy part of their value to society. Temporary personality aberrations are very common, indicating maladjustment to the stresses of living.[51] Carlson's diagram (Fig. 4) also shows the sharp deterioration of sexual vigor, somewhat more gradual losses of motility (motor ability), and extremely poor status throughout for cardiovascular and respiratory function reflecting in poor nutrition and metabolism. This appears to be the greatest dynamic health problem of

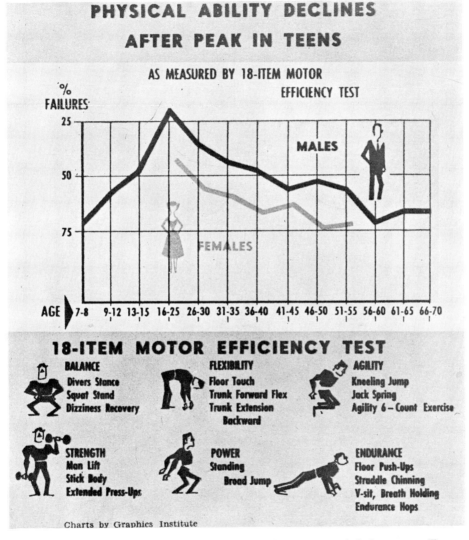

FIGURE 2A. Data from T. K. Cureton, Physical Fitness Research Laboratory. (From Pageant, Feb. 1959.)

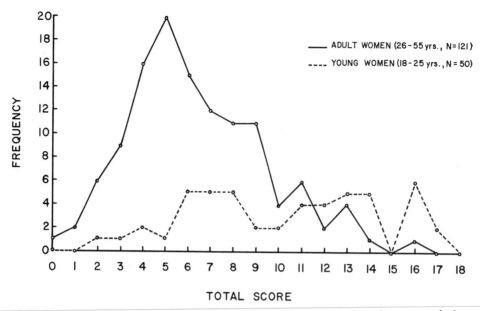

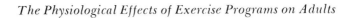

FIGURE 2B.   Eighteen-item Motor Efficiency Test. Frequency of total scores made by women. Physical Fitness Research Laboratory, U. of Ill.

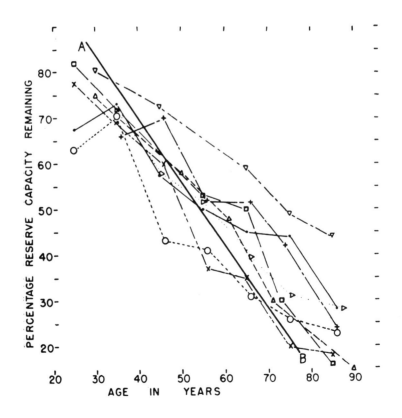

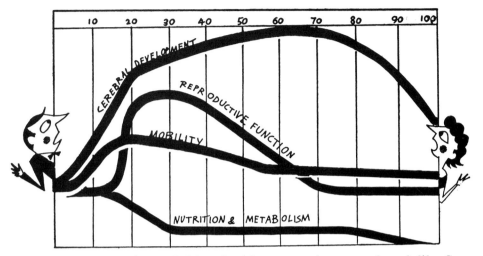

FIGURE 4. Rise and decline of vital functions show contrasting curves through life. Cerebral development remains high until advanced years because of improving judgment and accuracy. Sinking curve of metabolic process shows why older people should exercise more. "Mobility" refers to muscle and joint action. (From Coughlan, Robert [after Anton Carlson]: Now within sight: 100-year lifetime. *Life, 38* [No. 17], April 25, 1955.)

modern society. The use of food is highly related to the amount of exercise taken, thus governing to a large extent the nutritional state as well as the total circulatory-respiratory and glandular fitness. The training of the sympatho-adrenal system to resist stress is basic to dynamic health. Enough movement of the body—enough calories of work every day—is fundamental.

Parallel Decline of Many Physiological Aspects with Age and Loss of Physical Fitness

It is shown in Figure 3 in the data of Drs. Isaac Starr and Francis C. Wood, combined with data of Strehler and Mildvan, that when the body fails, many physiological systems fail together in a parallel way.[52] While these systems are anatomically considered separate, they are interlaced by nerves and blood vessels which react very similarly to stress, to internal temperature changes, to the common sharing of nutrition—which

←▨

FIGURE 3. Deterioration of vital functions with age. Solid line descending from upper left to lower right = acceleration wave of ballistocardiogram. Dotted lines descending essentially parallel to it are other physiological parameters. Triangles pointing down = standard cell water. Squares = standard renal plasma flow. Triangles pointing up = basal metabolic rate. X's = maximum breathing capacity. Dots = nerve conduction velocity. Circles = cardiac output per beat. Crosses = standard glomerular filtration rate. Triangles pointing right = vital capacity. (From Starr and Wood: Twenty-year studies with the ballistocardiograph. *Circulation, 23*:714-732, May 1961.) (Data from Strehler and Mildvan.)

has long been the thesis of Dr. Hans Selye[53] who has projected a common basis of disease. We have measured human stamina (with endurance tests) and its improvement, converse to deterioration. The several systems do react together as if some common factor united them; perhaps it is oxygen supply, or the common inter-reactivity of the nervous system. The proprioceptors affect the more central areas of the nervous system, and the brain reacts to effect movement or physiological responses, too complicated to describe in full.

It is interesting that the deterioration of the principal components of the central nervous system, acting through the motor abilities, do apparently deteriorate parallel to more internal physiological aspects, as shown in Figure 3. To evaluate the system, it is not absolutely necessary to measure every possible specific type of physiological response. As a person ages, or loses his physical fitness, the eyes fail, the sex life deteriorates, the muscular strength wanes related to weight, cells disappear, there is dehydration and shrinkage of the tissues, and metabolism slowly ebbs—and all this either during extreme losses of physical fitness or in the course of physiological aging.

Cureton tested middle-aged subjects on the treadmill (4-min jog: 7 mph, 8.6% grade) to the virtual limit of their ability (after some warm-

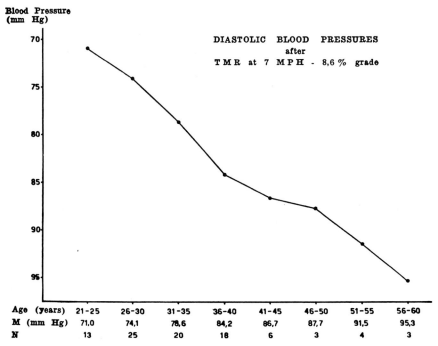

Age (years)	21-25	26-30	31-35	36-40	41-45	46-50	51-55	56-60
M (mm Hg)	71,0	74,1	78,6	84,2	86,7	87,7	91,5	95,3
N		13	25	20	18	6	3	4	3

FIGURE 5. Diastolic blood pressure, after exercise, increases steadily with age. (From Cureton, T. K.: *Med Sportiva*, 12:259-281, July 1958.)

up and preliminary preparation). Results shown in Figure 5 depict the steady increase with age in post-exercise blood pressure (diastolic) taken in the sitting position from 1 minute to 1 minute and 15 seconds after the 4-minute run.[54] This experiment reflects the tightening arterial system, which is much more definite in the relatively untrained rather than in the trained adults—and one sign of good arterial fitness is ability to keep the diastolic blood pressure relatively low in a standard or all-out exertion.

Recording the diastolic pressure after a standardized exertion is a good test to reflect the ability of the arterioles and capillaries to "drain off" the highly pressurized aortic tree after each systole of the heart. Unusual tenseness, lack of sufficient capillarization, or atherosclerosis would cause the vascular system to be sluggish in passing the blood on to the working tissues. In training middle-aged men, we have long noted that results of this test improve greatly but quite in proportion to the endurance work taken.

Deterioration of Personality Traits with Aging and Loss of Physical Fitness

Physical deterioration parallels the loss of muscular and cardiovascular functions, and both lead to loss of circulation, sluggishness, and poor defense against the stresses of heat, cold, and exertion. Dr. Josef Brozek[55] has reported the parallel loss of certain desirable personality traits with aging by comparing two hundred normal business and professional men averaging 50 years of age with 119 college students averaging 22 years of age.

The personality traits which usually change for the poorer with age and loss of physical fitness are (1) loss of physical courage, (2) less participation in dynamic (extroverted) activities (sports, exercise, physical work), (3) fear of personal exposure to weather (hot and cold), fear of loss of health and safety, (4) greater tension, introversion, and preoccupation with money, social status, competition, and responsibility. Such deterioration in the face of increased mental stress is now pronounced as a principal cause of heart disease, or at least fatigue and loss of zest for living *(cf.* Raab's *Prevention of Ischemic Heart Disease)*[56, 57]

In three studies in our physical education department at the University of Illinois, eight of Dr. Raymond B. Cattell's sixteen Personality Traits were significantly correlated with "all-out treadmill running ability." The traits which were negatively correlated with endurance were (1) sophistication; (2) fear for self (more sensitive to criticism); (3) anxiety; (4) sensitiveness to esthetic stimuli; (5) viscerotonic tendency to overeat, overdrink, overindulge in luxurious living; (6) cerebrotonic tendency (overconcern with intellectual pursuits); (7) mental fatigue symptoms, mental-physical disintegration (will power and ability of the body to follow the volitional desires); and (8) rigidity of personal conduct and "mental set" (unadjustable).[58]

Furthermore, it is interesting that Drs. Cattell, Jones and Kaplan, Walter Miles and Dr. Nancy Duggan point out the parallel trend for certain mental abilities to decline in patients after 25 years of age—abilities such as computational speed, memory, mental energy, mental adjustment to new situations, ability to learn to swim, and reasoning on new problems. But certain other mental abilities such as vocabulary, elements involving experience, and occupational learning may improve with age.[58]

Intimately tied up with the loss of personality traits is the parallel progressive deterioration shown by deviation from the youthful standard at 20 years of age which afflicts most adults as they age (Fig. 6). It is hard to say which has the greatest effect on one's total net life, socially, occupationally, intellectually, spiritually. It is the firm conviction of the writer, after a lifetime of study of the subject, that physical fitness is like the trunk of a tree which supports all the rest of the desirable aspects of life: energy, sex life, happiness, and fulfillment to normal expectancy as in youth. When one falls short of one's aspirations, then frustration, psychological depression, and withdrawal into relative inactivity may result, with one doing less and less to serve or benefit himself or others. This point of view has been fully expressed in *Physical Fitness and Dynamic Health*[59] and in the correlative publication, *The Healthy Life*.[60]

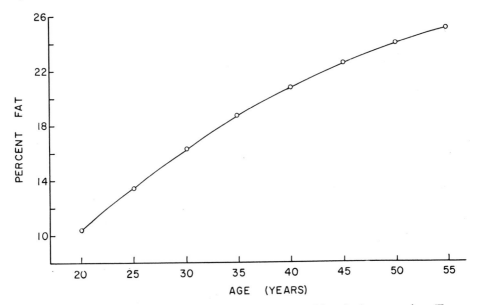

FIGURE 6. Averages of estimated changes in body composition during maturity. (From Brozek, J.: Changes of body composition in men during maturity and their nutritional implications. *Fed Proc, 11*:784, 1952.)

It is extremely hard to follow people through their whole lives to prove the case. Since very little of the long-range follow-up has been done—except perhaps on the large group comparative basis, as in epidemiology[61] where heart disease has come in for some long-range study—the missing link is in truly evaluating the amount and nature of exercise taken during the lifetime.

We must begin by experimentation to observe some of the immediate and short-range effects of exercise upon both the *general resistance* and upon specific physiological variables. It is impressive to observe, in families, the high correlative agreement of tests to deteriorate downward or to improve upward. This certainly suggests that families are interlinked through the nervous system, and possibly, too, through the circulatory-endocrine system. In the case of the tree, let something happen to the soil, or to the circulation in the trunk, and what have you? The nervous system is not so fully established in the tree, but *man* is distinguished by his nervous system, his mobility, and his understanding when compared to the tree. To the extent to which he uses his unique endowment, he can have *life*.

All society has been drifting away from hard work, the type done by our pioneer forefathers. Mechanical machines of all types have reduced physical labor. In this day and age, all kinds of gadgets, shaking chairs, vibrating couches, electrical massagers, in addition to pills, salts, and patent medicines, are devised to make people thin and healthy.

But in the face of the great activity of chemists and engineers to design gadgets which carry the halo of health, study after study shows that there is no easy way to improve the physical powers of the body, any more than there is an easy way to improve the mathematical powers of the mind. It has been discovered that even casually played sports, without emphasis upon repetitive work dosage, are relatively ineffective for developing muscle tone, oxygen intake capacity, endurance, and better circulation.

References

46. THE HEALTH LIFE. A *Life-Time* publication, 1966.
47. CURETON, T. K.: How to keep your family young. *Redbook, 104*:30-31, 90-91, April 1955.
48. SNYDER, JULIAN, and KNAUTH, PERCY: The tip that led Bannister to victory. *Sports Illustrated, 1*:6-9, August 30, 1954.
49. CURETON, T. K.: *Physical Fitness Workbook*. St. Louis, Mosby, 1947, pp. 31-32.
50. CURETON, T. K.: *Physical Fitness Appraisal and Guidance*. St. Louis, Mosby, 1947, pp. 390-423.
51. COUGHLAN, ROBERT: Now within sight: 100-year lifetime. *Life, 38*(No. 17), April 25, 1955.
52. STARR, ISAAC, and WOOD, F. C.: Twenty-year studies with the ballistocardiograph. *Circulation, 23*:714-732, May 1961).

53. Selye, Hans, *op. cit.* (refs. 13-16).

54. Cureton, T. K.: Post-exercise blood pressures in maximum exertion tests and relationships to performance time, oxygen intake and debt, and peripheral resistance. *Lancet, 77*:81-82, March 1957; and in *Med Sport (Roma), 12*:259-281, July 1958.

55. Brozek, Josef: Personality of young and middle-aged normal men. *J Geront 7*:410, July, 1952.

56. Raab, W., and Krzywanek, H. J.: Cardiac sympathetic tone and stress response related to personality patterns and exercise habits. In Raab, W. (Ed.): *Prevention of Ischemic Heart Disease,* Springfield, Thomas 1966, pp. 121-134.

57. Wolffe, J. B.: Situational stresses as cause of cardiovascular disease. In Raab, W. (Ed.): *Prevention of Ischemic Heart Disease.* Springfield, Thomas, pp. 208-211.

58. Cureton, T. K.: Improvement of psychological states by means of exercise-fitness programs. *J Phys Ment Rehab, 17*:14-25, Jan.-Feb. 1963.

59. Cureton, T. K.: *Physical Fitness and Dynamic Health.* New York, Dial, 1965.

60. The Healthy Life: A *Life-Time* publication, 1966.

61. Holloszy, John: The epidemiology of coronary heart disease: National differences and the role of physical activity. *Amer Geront Soc, 11*:718-725, August 1963.

IV

SPECIFIC EFFECTS OF PHYSICAL TRAINING UPON MIDDLE-AGED SUBJECTS

REDUCTION OF TOTAL PERIPHERAL RESISTANCE AND ARTERIAL VOLUME RIGIDITY

Peripheral Resistance and Load Upon the Heart

The effective load against which the heart works per beat is designated TPR, the total peripheral resistance as defined by Wiggers.[62] It cannot be exactly physically determined; but by indirect methods a close proportional evaluation may be made which is of considerable significance because of combining the training effects into one formula. Wiggers suggests a slightly simplified formula to that of Ralston, Guttentag, and Ogden.[63] We have also explored the relative validity and reliability of three formulae, all based upon approximate stroke volume determined from the heartograph, which method was found to correlate 0.88 with the Grollman stroke volume. Because both give values too low compared with catheterization methods, a constant of 38 cc per beat has been added to make an approximate correction, noting the parallel slope of the stroke volume curve related to age.[64, 65] From 1930 to 1936, nine authors used thirteen different types of equations, terminology, and units for TPR. Since circulation through the gross heart, lung, muscle circuit is 1/TPR, a reduction in TPR means that gross circulation has been improved. Reducing the TPR is the most effective means of increasing the circulation.

The Formula Used for TPR

It is pointed out in Bainbridge's *Physiology of Exercise*[66] that the output of the heart depends ultimately upon the contractility power of the fibers and rate of the beat per minute. The usual formula for cardiac output is the stroke volume times the rate. We decided to use a stroke volume determined from the amplitude of the heartograph stroke, using a chart arranged by Michael and Cureton to give a proportionate value and to multiply the stroke output by time per beat. The amplitude of the heartograph (and/or the derived stroke volume) is proportional to the force in the BCG, hence, Ft = MV. The force (proportional to amplitude) × time

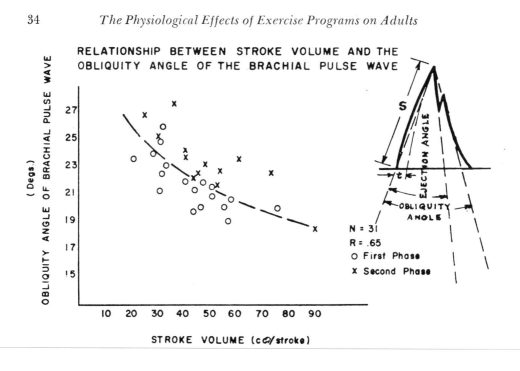

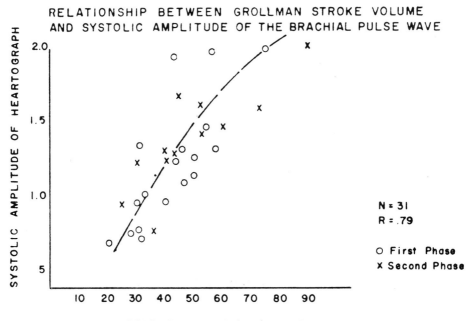

FIGURE 7A, B. Relationships between stroke volume and measures of brachial pulse wave. Physical Fitness Research Laboratory, U. of Ill. (Michael-Cureton).

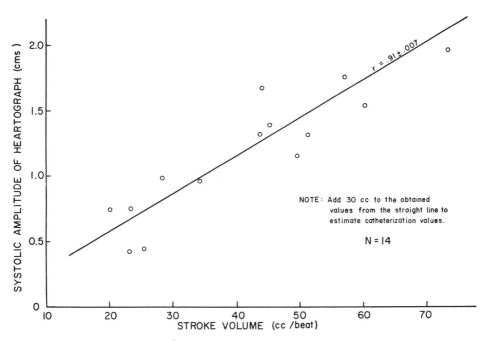

FIGURE 8.   Relation of systolic amplitude of heartograph to stroke volume of the heart. Physical Fitness Research Laboratory, U. of Ill. (Michael-Cureton, 1949).

per beat equals the momentum of the blood driven from the heart. Resistance to flow is quite proportional to velocity, assuming the aorta be a frictionless tube.

Therefore,

$$\text{TPR}_1 = \frac{\text{Systolic blood pressure (SBP)} + \text{Diastolic blood pressure (DBP)}/2}{\text{Stroke volume*} \times \text{Time per beat of the heart}^\dagger}$$

*The stroke volume is estimated from a conversion graph developed by Michael-Cureton to convert Grollman stroke volume to a stroke volume derived from this graph. By adding a statistical constant of 38 cc, the values can be corrected to those closely approximating catheterization values, but for simple statistical relative comparisons this is not absolutely necessary. (Refer to Figs. 7 and 8.)

†Taken as the heart rate/60, giving the time per beat.

By another calculation, the *volume elasticity* was reduced 36.7 per cent, which may be interpreted as an improvement in the suppleness of the arterial system, and the TPR indicates an improvement in reduction of *load on the heart* (i.e. resistance against which the heart works). The formula used for the *volume elasticity* calculation is as follows:

$P_s = V_s (TPR \times R + E/4)$, wherein, $P_s =$ Systolic pressure in mm Hg

and $E =$ Volume elasticity[66]

$V_s =$ Stroke volume from the Michael-Cureton chart in cc to which is added 38 (refer to Fig. 8).

$R =$ Heart rate$/60$

The use of stroke volume $\times$ time is similar to Starr's argument for a new energy unit of force $\times$ time to express the energy of the heart stroke.[67] High energy of ejection and low blood pressure indicate good circulation, and that is just what results from this formula.

Farhi[68] studied the relative net statistical contribution (proportional to Beta Squares in the Sewell Wright Path Coefficient System) of the principal contributing variables in the TPR formula and concluded after studying 152 male subjects from the files on middle-aged subjects at the University of Illinois that the TPR can be predicted from the stroke volume of the heartograph, taken while sitting, $(R = 0.87,$ S. E. $0.108)$ using the formula

$TPR = 2.71 - 0.18$ CO per beat

S.E. $= 0.18$

CO $=$ Cardiac output in cc per beat from the heartograph line chart of Michael-Cureton (*cf.* Fig. 8).

The net causal analysis statistical solution for the relative *net* contributions of each factor involved is as follows:

CO per beat from the heartograph chart $= 83.64\%$
Systolic blood pressure $= 8.92\%$
Diastolic blood pressure $= 7.27\%$
Heart rate $= 0.01\%$

Weight $= 0.06\%$
Ponderal index $= 0.06\%$
Height $= 0.03\%$
Age $= 0.01\%$

Results of Physical Training of Adults on the TPR

McAdam[69] determined the Grollman stroke volume on several middle-aged subjects, using two types of exercise: (1) a 5-Minute Step Test on a 17-inch bench, 30 steps per minute and (2) longitudinal training of 3 to 6 months with middle-aged subjects on progressive rhythmical exercises.

Cureton reported this work with his own comments.[70] An example was worked out on subject S.L.T., a 47-year-old subject who was trained for 6 months in a mixed-deck calisthenics and endurance swimming program at the University of Illinois. The formula TPR_1 was used.

Cureton took one hundred middle-aged men from the files at the

TABLE II

TOTAL PERIPHERAL RESISTANCE,

ADULT MALES (19 to 69 Yrs)

Standard Score	TPR_1	TPR_2	TPR_3	Formulas Used
100	0.70	0.57	0.53	$TPR_1 = \dfrac{SBP + DBP}{2}$
95	0.77	0.63	0.58	
90	0.83	0.69	0.64	cc/beat (taken from the Michael-Cureton graph, using
85	0.90	0.75	0.70	amplitude and converted
80	0.97	0.81	0.75	to CO)
75	1.03	0.87	0.81	
70	1.10	0.93	0.86	cc/beat = Cardiac output per beat
65	1.16	0.99	0.92	= Area under heartograph curve
60	1.23	1.05	0.98	+ 38 cc
55	1.29	1.11	1.03	$TPR_2 = \dfrac{SBP + DBP}{2}$
50	1.36	1.17	1.09	
45	1.43	1.23	1.15	cc/sec (Cardiac Output)
40	1.49	1.29	1.20	$TPR_3 = \dfrac{DBP + \frac{SBP - DBP}{3}}{}$
35	1.56	1.35	1.26	cc/sec (Cardiac Output)
30	1.62	1.41	1.32	
25	1.69	1.47	1.37	TPR = Total peripheral resistance
20	1.75	1.53	1.43	SBP = Systolic blood pressure (mm Hg)
15	1.82	1.59	1.49	
10	1.89	1.65	1.54	DBP = Diastolic blood pressure (mm Hg)
5	1.95	1.71	1.60	
0	2.02	1.77	1.65	CO/sec = Cardiac output per sec
M	1.36	1.17	1.09	= Area under curve + 38 cc ×
(SD)	0.219	0.200	0.188	HR/60
N	152	152	152	where HR = heart rate in
Range	0.85–	0.58–	0.54–	beats/min
	1.93	1.80	1.65	

(Note: SS calculations from data in Ph.D. thesis of Asher Farhi, 1965, University of Illinois. The three formulae are shown to correlate very highly together i.e. 2 and 3 correlated 0.995; and both of these, 2 and 3 correlated better than 0.60 with 1; but 1 is best because the systolic amplitude of the brachial pulse wave is used, which inserts velocity of the stroke into the ratio.)

University of Illinois Physical Fitness Laboratory and computed the peripheral resistance (TPR_1), using about every fifth case. The TPR_1 was plotted against age. The resulting curve is practically a straight line with TPR_1 going up steadily with age. Then by using the retest folders of these same men and heartographs therein, the TPR_1 was computed after the men had participated for one academic year (6 to 8 months) in the men's adult program. The peripheral resistance reduced impressively in these men, but it is perhaps of even greater significance that the differences be-

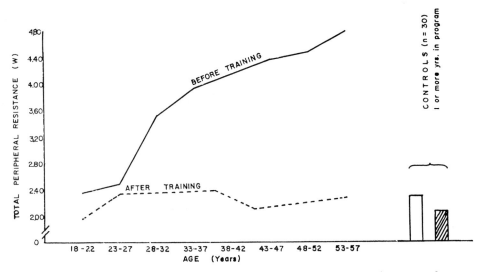

FIGURE 9. Reduction of total peripheral resistance by rhythmic continuous endurance work. *Data from Heartographs:* $W = P/(V_s \times t)$. $P =$ mean blood pressure, $V_s =$ stroke volume (conversion chart), $t =$ time (sec/beat). Mean age of 100 men studied: 43.7 years. Training: 7 months, 1 hour per day, 3 or 4 days per week doing running, swimming, calisthenics. Physical Fitness Research Laboratory, U. of Ill. (Cureton, 6/1/63).

tween the older and younger men were washed out (*cf.* Fig. 9). The program featured running, swimming, and rhythmic conditioning exercise for an hour per day, three to five times per week. Formula TPR_1 was used.[71] By substituting figures for the variables given in the formula above, the following results were obtained:

$$\textit{Pretraining: } TPR = \frac{155}{(29 + 38) \times 0.80} = 2.89 \text{ mm Hg per cc per sec}$$

wherein, Systolic BP $= 180$ mm Hg
Diastolic BP $= 130$ mm Hg

$V_s = 29$ cc per beat $+ 38$ (constant) $= 67$ cc
$t = 48/60 = 0.80$ sec per beat

$$\textit{Posttraining: } TPR = \frac{128}{(75 + 38) \times 0.867} = 1.32 \text{ mm Hg per cc per sec}$$

The results show a ratio of 1:2.19, an improvement of 100 per cent. Figure 10 shows that the 30-to-39-year group was most resistant to improvement.

Pallandi,[72] in a thesis under Cureton but doing the work at the Montreal YMCA, repeated this same type of experiment using a control group as well. The same types of changes took place in the thirty middle-aged

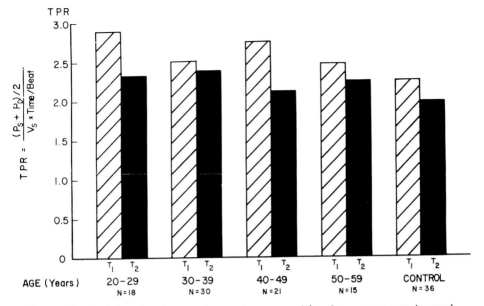

FIGURE 10. Peripheral resistance changes by age resulting from noon exercise work (120 middle-aged men). Physical Fitness Research Laboratory, U. of Ill. (Cureton).

TABLE III

REDUCTION IN TOTAL PERIPHERAL RESISTANCE IN MIDDLE-AGED MEN
(Pallandi-Cureton)

Test	*Units*	*Initial Test* (T_1)	*Final Test* (T_5)	*Significance* *(1% level)*	*Per Cent* *Change*
Systolic blood pressure	mm Hg	126	130	No	3.17%
Diastolic blood pressure	mm Hg	91	81	Yes	10.97%
Time per beat	sec	0.83	0.91	Yes	9.64%
Stroke volume (V_s)*	cc	26	41	Yes	57.69%
TPR_1	mm Hg per cc per sec	5.40	3.00	Yes	44.44%

*V_s was obtained from the Cameron heartograph and the use of the Michael-Cureton line chart, without adding 38 cc per beat. Poiscuille's Law gives

$$F = \frac{P\text{-}P_1 \times 1/n}{R},$$

where F = Rate of flow, P-P_1 = Pressure difference, R = Resistance, n = Viscosity factor, V_s = Stroke volume; and, from which Ralston, Guttentag, and Ogden analogously derive the formula,[73]

$$R = \frac{P_{mean}}{V_s \times \text{Pulse rate}/60}$$

Wiggers[74] derives the same formula.

subjects, who followed Cureton's progressive exercise system of running, rhythmic exercises, and deep breathing, three times per week for 16 weeks of training. Table III shows some of the results on the cardiovascular measures.

The great relative superiority of the progressive running, calisthenics, forced breathing system compared to the control group, the volleyball group, and the weight training group is also shown in this study.[136]

Implication of Changes in Total Peripheral Resistance

The results shown, as an example, in this section related to improving (lowering) TPR and E are in the opposite direction to the age changes reported by Brandfonbrenner, Landowne, and Shock.[75] Hence, they may be interpreted as reversals in physiological aging. Moreover, it is shown in other experiments with fairly similar methods that the TPR is greatly reduced during hard exercise—the harder the exercise, the greater the reduction.[76] All evidence suggests that capillaries open, probably due to the vasodilator nervous influence at the ends of the arterioles, where the small sphincter valves are stimulated to open.[77] It is conceded that there is very little change of flow through a particular capillary. Ring, Blum, and Kurbatov[78] state that in a trained runner like Roger Bannister there should be a capillary surface of approximately 64 square meters. Jokl[79] has reviewed Pretrén's evidence (1935 to 1939) that guinea pigs which are run hard and long on a treadmill daily will develop 40 to 45 per cent additional capillarization compared to sedentary animals not run in a similar way. Ogawa[80] confirmed the development of this "extra" capillarization. Uvnas[81] relates the extra capillarization to the stimulation provided by the vasodilation fibers of the sympathetic nervous system, and not the vagi. Other researchers attribute the extra capillarization to "the need" as explained in developing some degree of tissue hypoxia as the result of severe work.[82]

Further Generalization About the Capillarization Effect
of Hard Exercise

One principal effect of the proper kind of exercise is to keep the capillaries and arterioles open in the skeletal muscles, brain, working blood vessels, heart muscle, and quite likely in the glands as well. Exercising these structures is the method of keeping their blood channels open and functioning. If high-level performance is required, especially of the endurance type, such chanels *must* be opened up, inasmuch as athletic efficiency and endurance depend greatly upon circulatory-respiratory efficiency. An example should be mentioned. One man, well over fifty, could swim length after length of the pool easily without apparent fatigue. Upon testing him, it was found that he had a very brachial pulse wave and low TPR before and after exercise for a full minute in duration (running hard in place), and that his oxygen intake capacity was good in hard work, and his blood pressures were relatively low after endurance exertion. Another man, younger but who had also swum for many years, complained that he became severely tired. In fact, he was awlays badly out of breath after a length or two. In testing him, it was shown that his brachial pulse wave was much smaller and his TPR higher both before and after the same type of test exercise; his breath-holding time was shorter after exercise; his blood presssures were higher after a hard test exercise; and his oxygen intake under work on the treadmill was lower. Here we have the real difference as to why the exercise is easy for one man and hard for the other. The first man has good circulation, no doubt because of better blood flow *and* because the blood can get through the capillary beds in the muscles and lungs and heart relatively quickly, and TPR is unquestionably lower. The most critical aspect of this combined circulatory-respiratory fitness is probably what has been called, in the physiological literature, capillarization or collateral circulation in the heart.

It is not very commonly known that the nerves to the capillaries and other small blood vessels so completely control the circulatory turnover. The physiology of this is very complicated because the small vessels are under the influence of the autonomic nervous system.[83, 84] At rest it may be that nervous tension acts to close up (constrict) the vessels. During exercise, the sympathetic branch of the autonomic nervous system usually will act to constrict the skin vessels and open (dilate) the small vessels in the heart, muscles, and lungs.[85, 86]

SHRINKAGE IN HEART SIZE WITH PHYSICAL TRAINING IN MIDDLE-AGED MEN

An Example

A study was made of three business executives, who were found to have enlarged hearts during routine examinations by 6-foot x-ray mensuration, using the Ungerleider-Clark tables and nomogram (Equitable Life Insurance Company).[87] Keys and Friedell[88] had shown that athletic men were distinguished from nonathletic men at the same age level not by heart size but by *stroke volume* as measured by the kymogram-x-ray method. Cureton's data on top Olympic athletes[89] showed that heart size differed insignificantly from normal men of the same age in the same team sport, that is, swimmers as a team group did not differ in average from normal young men, with a group of 101 men taken from the University of Illinois population as the control group. But these athletes had taller, sharper, brachial pulse waves as taken on the Cameron Heartometer machine.[90] This would agree in effect with the position of Keys and Friedell. The vertical dimension of the brachial pulse waves indicates stroke volume, not heart rate.

The three middle-aged men, aged fifty (R.L.), fifty-one (F.H.B.), and sixty-one (H.C.B.) were tested in the university hospital and in the Physical Fitness Research Laboratory. They were put on a progressive program of rhythmic endurance exercises. Over a period of a year, combining calisthenics, walking, and swimming for 1 hour average per day, their hearts reduced in size 8.06, 21.6, and 8.15 percent, respectively, on the endurance program. The data and x-rays were presented at scientific meetings and published in full by Cureton.[91] There is no question about hearts of some young athletes enlarging with an excessive amount of endurance work, as has been shown by Herxheimer,[92] and by Reindell.[93] Prominent sports' doctors put the blame upon sports for enlarging the hearts of athletes.[94, 95] Dr. Tanner of Finland found among athletes some enlarged hearts which returned to normal after a year or two of de-training from strenuous endurance sports.[96]

A second study was carried out by Phillips and Cureton[97] on middle-aged men with the same methods. A correlation was shown between heart size and age in the data at Urbana of 0.359 ± 0.0439, showing a trend toward enlargement of the heart with age. A reversal of this trend would indicate a reversal toward youthfulness, especially if the BCG_v and BCG_a measures also increased in physical training. Since the completion of the first work by Cureton and the follow-up study by Phillips and Cureton, it was shown that the BCG waves did increase in amplitude, velocity, and acceleration in a study by Holloszy, Skinner, Barry and Cureton, also at Urbana.[98] Holmgren and associates reported a confirming study in 1961.[99]

Reasons for Reduction

Several physiological reasons may be advanced as to why the physical training reduced the heart size in the middle-aged men: (1) They were debilitated, rather aged, and had poor circulation at the beginning of the experiment. (2) They used physical training work which has been shown in many studies to increase the circulation, vigor of the heart stroke (because of more blood passing through the heart), and oxygen intake capacity. While the maximal O_2 intake was not measured at the time and only substitute tests were used, it has since been shown by Naughton[100] and Ribisl[101] that maximal oxygen intake is increased in a similar program by about 20 percent in an initial course of physical training— thus, it may be assumed that O_2 intake capacity had increased. (3) Basal metabolic rate increased during the training, and this alone may have accounted for some reduction in heart size. (4) Studies by Gualtiere[102] have also shown that young adult subjects in training usually increase their blood volume in circulation.

It may be said in summary that the sympatho-adrenal system was tuned up by the training, basal metabolic rate was increased, and much better circulation developed with less stasis in the veins and venous pools in the

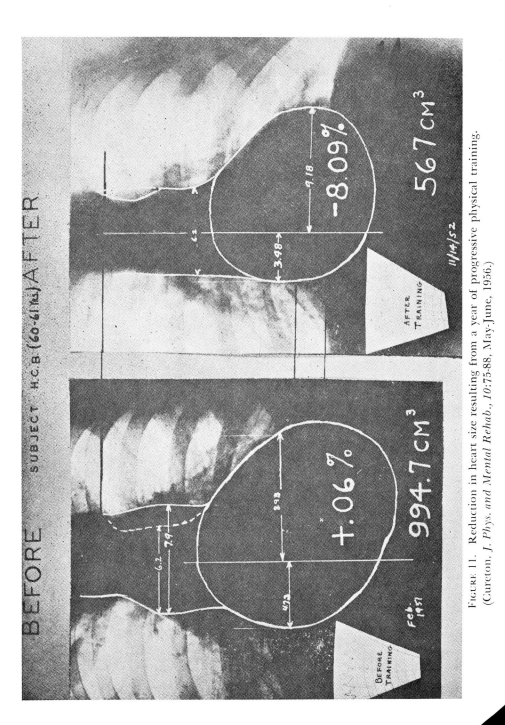

FIGURE 11. Reduction in heart size resulting from a year of progressive physical training. (Cureton, *J. Phys. and Mental Rehab.*, 10:75-88, May-June, 1956.)

splanchnic region and large leg veins, and also possibly in the lungs.[103] By keeping the blood in more continuous circulation, there is a tendency to reduce the amount which accumulates in the right heart and lungs, and in the abdominal and leg veins.

Perhaps some fat around the heart was reduced, which was not measured, but the endurance and heart function tests were much improved. The finding that the heart size is reduced by endurance training in such older men is a relatively new and unique one.

SYMPATHETIC VERSUS PARASYMPATHETICOTONIC EFFECTS, AND NORMALIZATION

Sympatheticotonic Versus Parasympatheticotonic Responses to Training

Moderate exercise, adapted to the needs of the individual, will usually result in a beneficial regulatory improvement in the autonomic nervous system. The shift may occur in two ways: (1) increased vagus tone and slower pulse rate and (2) increased vigor in the vertical inotropic deflections of the heartograph, ballistocardiograph, and T-waves of the electrocardiogram at rest. But also, the systolic blood pressure may go up, the basal metabolic rate may increase, the pulse pressure will increase, and the various nervous reflexes and nerve propagation speeds will increase—all indicating an increase in the sympatheticotonic responses in the nervous system *at rest* if the program is *progressive,* leaving the nervous system reflecting the stress effects, just as if it has memory, as it does according to Gellhorn.[104] The pattern of these effects is shown in Table IV.

Effect of Rhythmic Versus Tensing Type Programs

Moderate programs conducted in the submaximal or steady state, if long practiced (with less than 3 liters of net oxygen debt), often result in rather complete adaptation; and the stress effects of performing a given submaximal task may be less after a course in physical training than before such training. This might show less oxygen cost for the given piece of work, slower pulse rate, and even smaller vertical deflections of all types in the ECG, BCG, heartograph measurements. While this is usually true, *hard training* programs—to which full adaptation is not made, and especially when the effects of the day's training are reflected "around the clock" and may last several

    a nervous disturbance—will usually leave the subject in the
    nic type of dominance. How long this may last is quite vari-
    rent subjects, but experiments have shown that Schneider
    y be depressed for as long as 2 weeks[105] following the running
    plechase course to which the subjects were not gradually
    xperienced endurance athletes may, therefore, appear to be
    ed than normal subjects and may show less disturbance of

TABLE IV

TYPICAL SHIFTS IN AUTONOMIC NERVOUS SYSTEM MEASURES (AT REST)
RESULTING FROM PROGRESSIVE PHYSICAL TRAINING

Parasympatheticotonic Phenomena	Test Involved	Sympatheticotonic Phenomena
Decreases	pulse pressure	increases
Increases or decreases (variable)	systolic blood pressure	increases
Increases	diastolic blood pressure	decreases
Increases or decreases (variable)*	pulse rate	increases or decreases (variable)*
Decreases	pulse pressure × rate	increases
Decreases	per beat stroke volume of heart	increases
Decreases	minute volume of the heart	increases
Faster (vessels tenser)	pulse wave transmission time	slower (vessels more relaxed with greater excursion)
Decreases	amplitude of the precordial T-waves of the ECG	increases
Decreases	basal metabolic rate	increases
Slower	nervous reflexes	faster
Smaller	diameter or area of the pupils of the eyes	larger
Slower	flicker fusion frequency	faster

* Quite variable depending upon the habituation of the nervous system to the effort, especially the amount of sympatho-adrenergic disturbance and time of recovery. Mild, long-continued programs, which are classified as submaximal, have parasympatheticotonic effects.

the ANS (autonomic nervous system); nevertheless, if these subjects go all-out in a race or trial beyond what they usually do, they may also show the effects of a sympatheticotonic character. Exercise upsets the homeostasis of untrained subjects very much and affects seasoned, long-trained people relatively less.[106, 107, 108] The Phillips-Cureton[108] experiment shows that discontinuing the training for 8 weeks, after 8 weeks of training, causes a loss of more than half of the improvements made.

The effects of training follow the laws of Selye's "adaptation syndrome" in the three major stages: (1) alarm (sympatheticotonic disturbances, which may or may not subside at rest). (2) adaptation (relatively less sympatheticotonic disturbance, more recovery during work, faster recovery). Selye also describes this stage as the period in which *general resistance* develops. (3) *incomplete adaptation* (in which fatigue accumulates and results in progressive deterioration, that is, staleness, loss of protein in the tissues, reduction in blood sugar, and even collapse if the work is harder than can be adjusted over an extended period of overload. Such staleness is commonly seen in athletes, and it may occur in regular conditioning work, also, when middle-aged men go too hard in too short a period to permit a gradual adaptation. Men should be cautious for a month or two before working too hard, and they should get a bit more sleep during the first 8 weeks, at least after starting a program. After the first 2 months, there should be a letdown—perhaps a change to games, walking, or swimming for 2 weeks—then a harder period of work than before. One of our best results was in a program involving 8 weeks of work, followed by 8 weeks of walking and casual recreation, and then 8 weeks again of hard work.[108]   (Refer to Figs. 15 and 16.)

An Example Contrasting Two Types of Training

The influence of a *progressive* training program on the cardiovascular measurements is shown in Table V, taken from an experiment by du Toit[110] working with Cureton at the University of Illinois Physical Fitness Research Laboratory in Urbana, in 1965 and 1966. Two groups, a weight training group and a running group, trained for an hour, three times per week. The same amount of time was spent by both groups. The changes are impressively greater for the running group compared to the weight training group. There was a greater reduction in pulse rate, diastolic pressure, and a greater increase in amplitude and area of the brachial pulse wave, pulse pressure, Erlanger-Hooker Index (energy of circulation), amplitude of the T-wave, and basal oxygen consumption for the running group (basal metabolic rate). These changes indicate that the vagus tone was probably increased at rest (judging by lowered pulse rate) but all other changes in the running group indicate "sympathetic tuning," as Gellhorn speaks of it.[111] In middle-aged men with relatively low metabolic rates, it is an advantage to raise the metabolic rate, which has occurred in the running group, but this was lowered in the weight training group.

Interpretation of Changes

To explain the shift of autonomic tone to sympathetic in a hard-trained group, not fully adapted to the work or rested enough in gradual on-and-off rhythm, it is interesting to note what Gellhorn[112] states:

> When both the sympathetic and parasympathetic systems are stimulated, the sympathetic is dominant in normals—there is normal rather than depressed blood sugar (p. 63).
>
> A fall in diastolic pressure (usually with wider pulse pressure) leads to increased sympatho-adrenal discharges (p. 64).
>
> In the trained state there is elevated blood sugar and insulin, ready for fight or flight—indicating sympathetic dominance and better metabolic use of food and

TABLE V

CARDIOVASCULAR MEASURES OF EXPERIMENTAL SUBJECTS

(Running versus Weight Training Group)

Subjects	Pulse Rate (b/min)		Systolic BP (mm Hg)		Diastolic BP (mm Hg)		S. Amplitude of Pulse Wave (cm)		Area Under Pulse Wave (cm)		Pulse Pressure (mm Hg)		PP × PR (beats × mm Hg)		T-wave Amplitude (cm)		Basal O$_2$ Consumption (cc)	
	T_1	T_2	T_1	T_2	T_1	T_2	T_1	T_2	T_1	T_2	T_1	T_2	T_1	T_2	T_1	T_2	T_1	T_2
Weight Training Subjects																		
Si	60	52	115	108	78	80	.76	.85	.23	.25	37	28	2220	1456	.20	.29	340	350
Ca	60	60	108	102	80	78	.89	.95	.20	.23	28	24	1680	1440	.29	.28	335	345
La	70	72	120	118	80	80	.80	.90	.24	.26	40	38	2800	2736	.23	.25	380	360
So	62	60	105	106	78	82	.90	.99	.21	.22	27	24	1674	1440	.23	.28	390	295
Mi	56	56	108	106	70	70	1.10	1.10	.25	.26	38	36	2128	2016	.28	.29	145	150
He	60	60	110	108	80	78	.82	.80	.18	.19	30	30	1800	1800	.20	.22	246	240
Be	60	60	112	110	76	74	.83	.81	.20	.21	36	36	2160	2160	.23	.23	260	270
Ki	64	60	108	105	78	75	.87	.89	.18	.20	30	30	1920	1800	.14	.15	295	305
Mean	61	60	110	106	77	77	.87	.91	.21	.22	33	28	2045	1769	.21	.24	311	264
Running Subjects																		
As	84	72	140	135	90	84	.85	1.5	.20	.40	50	51	4200	3672	.18	.21	200	220
Ba	60	48	132	122	95	80	1.00	1.20	.20	.28	37	42	2220	2016	.30	.45	230	320
Co	80	80	126	125	93	80	.53	.59	.12	.17	33	45	2640	3600	.37	.41	327	380
Es	68	60	112	115	90	80	.97	—	.16	—	22	35	1496	2100	.10	.18	210	270
Ve	66	58	120	125	100	90	1.02	1.20	.25	.31	20	35	1320	2030	.10	.18	350	350
Li	68	64	106	112	76	86	.80	1.01	.20	.25	30	26	2040	1664	.10	.20	252	280
Nu	70	60	106	116	70	65	.80	1.10	.20	.30	36	51	2520	3060	.20	.30	250	275
Wr	64	60	116	120	88	82	1.01	1.36	.25	.30	28	38	1792	2880	.15	.19	145	190
Mean	70	62	119	121	88	81	.87	1.14	.20	.29	32	40	2153	2353	.21	.27	245	286

Note: Since the relative improvements of the weight training group and the running group are compared with respect to sympatho-adrenergic changes attributable to the training program, it may be noted that the mean for the systolic amplitude of the pulse wave, area under the pulse wave, pulse pressure, Erlanger-Hooker Index (PP × PR) and T-wave are practically identical at T_1 and are considered closely enough at the same starting level. The average level of sympatho-adrenergic fitness averaged 41 SS for the weight lifting group and 57 SS for the running group after the training (DuToit and Cureton, U. of Ill.).

oxygen. (Author's note—results in greater circulation of adrenaline and nor-adrenaline) (pp. 68-69).

Sympathetic tuning may be persistent as after effect, as in "memory" (p. 72).

During the anoxic state there is exaggerated sympathetic tuning which tends to remain as a persistent effect (p. 75).

Proprioceptive stimuli greatly stimulate the post-hypothalamic area, hence, induces sympathetic stimulation (p. 111).

Forbes Carlile[113] published the data taken on the Australian swimming team while at Townsville for the last 2 months of their training for the 1960 Olympic Games. There was an increase in the average, resting systolic blood pressure from 116 to 126 in the first 8 weeks, along with decreases in the diastolic pressure and an increase in pulse pressures. The males improved an average of twenty-eight standard scores in amplitude of the brachial pulse wave; the females improved twenty-eight standard scores. These Australian swimmers were clearly superior to the American swimmers of 1948 and the Japanese swimmers of 1936 reported by Cureton.[114, 115] The weight of the Australian swimmers remained the same at an average of 173 pounds throughout the 8 weeks. The precordial T-waves and R-waves indicated fatigue by being depressed in several swimmers, after which the work load was eased. Under the hardest training there were distortions in the T-waves, a flattening, and some increase in pulse rates, indicating sympathetic disturbance. This has been corroborated by Rose and Dunn.[116, 117] The Rose and Dunn telemetering work has shown a slowing of the pulse rate after repetitious bouts of 440-yard intervals in track training, and also has shown enlarged T-waves with warm-up and depressed T-waves with exhaustion.

Measurements Used to Determine the Pre-ejection Intervals

Figure 12 shows the measurements which were used in this experiment, and Table V shows the correlative cardiovascular measurements made upon the subjects. Pulse rate is, of course, taken as the entire length of the heart beat cycle, including the pre-ejection intervals and the pulse wave. The interval EML (electro-mechanical lag) is reputed to reflect the time required for the spread of the nerve currents from Q (beginning of stimulus), across the auricles, down through the bundle of His, and on through the branch bundle nerves to the myocardium. The interval ICP (isovolumic period) is reputed to reflect the sympathetic stimulation coming to the left ventricle by way of the sympathetic nerves. Then follows the actual ejection of blood shown as a pulse wave.

While the usual method to determine the TP (tension period) has been to use the beginning upsurge of the carotid pulse wave as the signal for blood being ejected from the heart, it may also be taken from the BCG at H' using the A (acceleration) tracing. The entire TP can be measured hori-

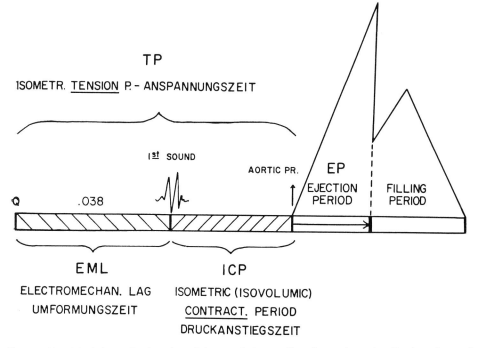

FIGURE 12.   Training, physical inactivity, and the cardiac dynamic cycle. Designations of subsections of left ventrical cardiac dynamic cycle.   (From Raab.)

zontally from the Q wave of the QRS complex to the point of the base-line crossing from G′ to H′ of the velocity curve (Fig. 13).

The splitting of the TP interval into the EML and the ICP intervals is indicated on the assumption that ICP is more sensitive and more purely reflects the sympathetic nervous stimulus to the heart. Whether this is so cannot be said with great finality. The EML interval is less sensitive, but it shortens under a strong adrenosympathetic stimulus such as hard exercise. Hyman[118] has reported that EML shortens under the influence of athletic training and lengthens in aging and in certain types of illness. The ICP lengthens in the relaxation state and shortens under adrenosympathetic stimulation; in complete adaptation to moderate exercise, it lengthens.

These measures help to interpret what is happening to an individual who goes into a longitudinal type of physical training or just as an immediate postexercise effect. In the experiment referred to by Du Toit-Cureton at the University of Illinois, there is a shift toward *higher relative sympathetic tone* in the peripheral circulation, but there is a relaxation in the sympathetic stimuli to the heart muscle (left ventricle) as indicated by a lengthening of ICP. This has also been found in various other experiments. This has been interpreted by Dr. Wilhelm Raab[119, 120, 121] as a very beneficial effect, con-

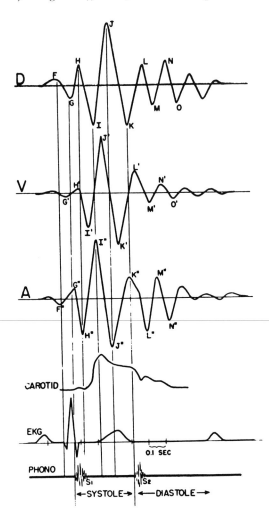

FIGURE 13. *G* to *H* crossing of base line as beginning of movement of blood out of the heart. Normal displacement *D*, velocity *V*, and acceleration *A* ballistocardiogram from a direct body system to show their relationship to each other and to the carotid pulse, electrocardiogram, and phonocardiogram. The tips of the *G* and *G″*, *H* and *H″*, *I* and *I″*, *J* and *J″*, *M* and *M″* waves coincide in time. At each of these points, velocity is zero (base-line crossing). (From Scarborough, W. R., and Talbot, S. A.: *Circulation*, 14:435-449, 1960. Also previous report by Rappaport in *Amer Heart J*, Dec. 1956.)

sidered protective against heart disease. Since we have experimented with several types of programs, additional comment may be made.

Reciprocal effects are probably taking place, that is, dilatation of the peripheral capillary beds takes the pressure (load) off the heart by lowering the peripheral resistance; as peripheral vasodilator nerves become active, there may be the reciprocal effect of diminishing the stimuli required to drive the heart (left ventricle). Raab has attributed the enlarged pulse waves resulting from progressive physical training programs to more blood flow through the heart, better venous return, and, in accordance with Starling's Law of the heart, greater end-diastolic pressure and greater relative ejection. We have tested this thesis in several ways. The intercorrelations do show that slow pulse rate is correlated with larger ejection waves; but ICP and EML are not correlated with performance in terms of all-out bicycle rides,[122] nor are these intervals correlated with peripheral phenomena such as blood flow (Erlanger-Hooker Index), brachial pulse waves, pulse pressure, or basal metabolic rate. They seem to be quite unique, but they shorten at once in response to an exercise which stirs up greater relative sympatho-adrenergic stimulation (as in stepping up and down on a bench, 2 minutes at 30 steps per minute). Thus, the immediate postexercise effect is very different from the longitudinal effect. Provided the latter is not overdone, a "tuning" (tone) may result peripherally, and a relaxation may result within the heart's left ventricle.

But we have also noted the programs as different as weight training and jogging produce very dissimilar effects. Jogging tends to lengthen the ICP and relieve the heart of some of the sympatho-adrenergic effect, but weight training does *not* do this, the ICP remaining as short as ever.[123]

Good correlations between post-exercise pulse rate (taken immediately at the end of the exercise) have been found with eosinopenia, rate of oxygen debt (liter/min/kg), and oxygen debt. But none of the pre-ejection intervals is significantly correlated with these commonly used stress indicators. The peripherally taken stress indicators are highly correlated with all-out tread-mill running time. This suggests that the sympathetic heart nerves stand by themselves. This is corroborated by experiments which have involved severing the sympathetic nerves to the heart of dogs, with no serious loss in working capacity.[124]

The author has contended that the vertical (inotropic) deflections of the heart stroke in the quiet state are augmented by sympatho-adrenergic stimuli.[125] The brachial pulse waves were shown to become taller and sharper about 1 to 2 minutes after adrenaline injections in a male subject sitting quietly at rest. The increase in vertical amplitude of the brachial pulse waves, in the T-waves of the precordial ECG waves, and in BCG deflections has been noted in many experiments.[126, 127, 128] Jokl and Wells[129] deflections indicated increased "sympathetic tuning." Mental excitement will also increase the amplitude.

USE OF EXERCISE TO REDUCE FAT, CHOLESTEROL, TRIGLYCERIDES, PHOSPHOLIPIDS

Reduction of Cholesterol, Phospholipids, and Triglycerides by Exercise Programs

Exercise may reduce cholesterol in the blood serum under certain conditions of the work done being long enough and hard enough. The data at this time of writing of some ten studies show that easy (*low gear*) programs are relatively ineffective, that is, programs in which exercise is at a comfortable level on vibrating tables, passively ridden bicycles, and even on low-resistance bicycles or other apparatus, and when the rate is so low as to fail to develop a full circulation and energy cost of more than five or six times the quiet-resting metabolic rate.[130, 131] This applies similarly to bowling, golf, quoits, leisurely walking, casual swimming, and all slow and intermittently played games such as softball, volleyball, and badminton.[36, 46, 136]

Some reductions are obtained in more strenuous activities (*middle gear*), such as walking in the semi-racing or racing style, interval style walk-jog, distance running, and games like tennis, handball, and squash. Included in this group would be games which combine as warm-up a good 30-minute preliminary period of calisthenics and running, and distance work in swimming, skiing, cycling, rowing and paddling, and hiking. In all of these, the work done for an hour or more begins to count. The consistency of the effort on a day-to-day basis, continued more than 6 weeks in a persistent program of 5 days or more per week, is a great factor too.

The best programs so far are of the continuous nonstop rhythmical type such as running, swimming, skating, skiing, cycling, hiking, and competitive games in which weight is lost and a negative caloric state is induced. Our recommendation is 5 to 6 days of work per week of 1 hour daily, or three or more longer workouts of $1\frac{1}{2}$ to 3 hours every-other day. Certain studies indicate that it is not only the length of the workout but the intensity (rate) of the work that is important.

Keys and associates reported that exercise would not reduce cholesterol if the subjects were held in caloric balance. Our position is that if the exercise is hard enough to invoke the adrenal glands, or hard enough to develop a second wind, then if such a program is repeated time and time again as a steady routine, results may reasonably be expected provided the cholesterol was high to begin with. In several of our studies, it is clear that thin-type (ectomorph) subjects do not change much, possibly because they are of negative or in-balance caloric types to begin with; whereas, subjects of positive caloric balance will usually reduce the cholesterol levels with almost any type of endurance exercise. This individualized nature of the situation is dominant as a rule and is even more important than the exact nature of the exercise.

A review of the studies completed on humans to date shows that in the Chailley-Bert and Fabre-Chevalier[132] and Montoye, Van Huss *et al.* work,[133] which we classify as easy to very moderate, the statistically insignificant reduction obtained was 41 to 35 mg per 100 cc, respectively. In Pohndorf's experiment[134] of swimming 1,000 yards per day, his male (M.D.) subject reduced 70, and his female (M.D.) subject reduced 40 mg per 100 cc. In Métivier's[135] work (32 sessions, three times per week for 50 to 60 minutes) with the vibrating table, the Exercycle, and the resistance bicycle, there were no significant reductions; but with four women in Cureton's progressive calisthenics and interval running program (1 hour, 3 times per week), all four women subjects reduced the cholesterol: 30.5 (sig.), 12, 9, and 14 mg per 100 cc. In this Cureton-led program, the gym work was done only once a week, and the women exercised at home at least two other days. Improvements were greater in the all-out treadmill run (18.75 SS), adipose tissue (13.75 SS), and terminal pulse rate (6.12 SS), than in the other three programs. Campbell[136] also found that programs of the Cureton type (continuous, rhythmical work with much bending of the arms and legs) produced greater reduction in cholesterol than activities like weight lifting and intermittently played games. Golding[137, 138] obtained the best reductions with what we classify as a hard (*high gear*) program with exercises done every day to the all-out level, cross-country running (this an hour at least) and then addition of handball for another 30 minutes. The progressive nature of this program was featured. The work was hard from the beginning with 20 to 30 minutes of hard all-out exercises, then the cross-country run for another 30 minutes was made faster and faster as the program went along for 25 weeks. This was a much longer and harder program than Montoye *et al.* conducted, and harder than that of Métivier or Pohndorf. Even Rochelle's program with young men was only 4 weeks long and consisted of running 2 miles per day, 5 days per week for time. Rochelle's[139] reductions were only 22.3 mg per 100 cc. This seems to indicate that even if a program is hard, it must last long enough and must total enough kilocalories of work to bring about the reduction. This is the trouble with some of the "spurty" games. The many rest periods in a game allow the metabolism to sag, after working it up, and the total of kilocalories of work is smaller than most realize.

Johnson and Wong's[140] experiment seems to show that cholesterol can also be measured too soon after a strenuous event to get the maximal reduction which should be attributed to the event. Their first experiment gave 186.6 mg per 100 cc for twelve young men before a swimming meet, then 188.1 after the meet; but the next morning these same men averaged 163.0 mg per 100 cc. In a second group of nine varsity swimmers who started the experiment at an average of 228, the results were 240 and 197 for the same conditions. The reduction of 23.6 mg per 100 cc is no doubt related to the strenuousness of the efforts, the short total time of the effort; even when the levels were higher to begin with, the reduction was only 31 mg per 100 cc. The normal controls did not change, nor did men who were put in the water for 3 minutes.

While cholesterol is shown to reduce quite usually if the work is hard enough to reduce the weight, Golding[141] has also shown that the reductions parallel improvements in strength, amplitude of the brachial pulse wave (heartograph), vital capacity residual, adipose tissue, specific gravity, 5-minute pulse recuperation counts, and postexercise blood pressure. The cholesterol change is not, therefore, a specific change but is related to all of the metabolic and fitness changes induced by a composite training effect. This is the basis for saying that the cholesterol change is a reflection of the total work done within a period of time, and that the net effect seems to be one of total metabolic involvement.

While dieting will reduce cholesterol if the total number of calories is reduced and animal fats (saturated with hydrogen) are replaced by polyunsaturated fats (sunflower seed oil, soybean oil, rapeseed oil, or wheat germ oil), including the replacement of butter with margarines, this does not lead to the increase in total body metabolism as does exercise. Since physical fitness depends primarily upon the increase in circulatory-respiratory capacity, strength, and reduction of fat, consistent programs of exercise over long periods of time—and for all of life—seem to be a much sounder approach than periods of dieting alone without exercise. The study of G. V. Mann at Harvard[142] demonstrated over 10 weeks on three subjects that doubling the calorie supply had no effects on the serum lipids as long as the excess of energy was dissipated through exercise. When exercise was restricted and fat deposition occurred, the serum cholesterol concentrations were doubled. Weight reduction by food restriction promptly returned the values to normal. From the point of view of physical education, it is important to note that once the food reduction had caused the weight to reduce and the cholesterol levels to come down to normal, then exercise of the right type, intensity, and duration would keep the serum cholesterol levels down even when the caloric intake was doubled. This makes it plain that people who eat abundantly must exercise. The nature of exercise that is hard enough and long enough is all-important.

The mechanisms by which exercise affects cholesterol reduction are not settled as yet beyond the principle already stated, "The total work done in the time." Kritchevsky[143] states that the liver is centrally involved and that the circulation of the cholesterol-protein complexes is by way of the lymphatics and veins and back into the blood. Exercise is known to influence greatly both the lymphatic circulation and the efficiency of the veins.

It is possible that the massaging action of muscles prevents some of the cholesterol deposition within the walls and on the walls of the blood vessels, an idea advanced by Dr. Irving Page.[144] Dr. Edward Bortz[145] also emphasizes that in the sluggish circulation there is more opportunity for cholesterol and its related triglycerides and fatty acids to deposit within the blood vessels. An idea consistent with the facts is that hard exercise involves the adrenal function, whereas, easy exercise usually does not. The adrenal glands lower cholesterol by converting it to corticosteroids. Powers and Diluzio[146] were able to show that the adrenals make a definite contribution to the regulation of the plasma lipid and cholesterol metabolism. Hurxthal[147] found lower cholesterol levels in hyperthyroidism, and Kritchevsky[143] is of the opinion that it is associated with a lack of the male hormone, androgen. Cureton[148] has also reviewed the effect of exercise on the glandular functions and shows data to indicate that basal metabolic rate is increased by hard and long exercise, at least in the period of hard training.

Our latest study by Skinner[149] shows that even with moderate reduction of cholesterol there is a large reduction of the triglycerides, from which cholesterol is synthesized within the body. Several writers have advanced the idea that it is more important to prevent the synthesis within the body than to eliminate the intake of cholesterol by way of reducing animal fats and proteins, and dairy foods. At least it seems safe to eat these foods if a strong exercise program is followed. In more recent work Garrett, Pangle, and Mann[150] used Cureton's rhythmic exercise program at George Peabody College and Vanderbilt Medical School, in Nashville, to confirm the cholesterol reduction in 6 weeks, followed by 6 weeks of de-training.

Part of the circulating sterol is withdrawn by the liver for utilization or degradation. Physical activity, by greatly increasing the circulation and metabolism, speeds up the processes of cholesterol excretion and also prevents synthesis of the sterol by reduction of the glycerides.

The Value of Hard Work, Endurance Type, to Reduce Fat, Cholesterol, Triglycerides, and Phospholipids of Blood Serum

A large number of experiments show that people extremely out of condition cannot easily adjust to hard exercise. It has been demonstrated that a gradually progressive system works; and if an educational program is carried along with the introductory exercise to show participants how absolutely essential it is to get up to high levels of effort, and to build up the total calories of work per day, per week, and per year, it will work with many subjects. We do not believe that this can be done well without leadership.

Fat is correlated negatively with many activities, but most of all with endurance activities such as long distance running activities; it i poorly correlated with short speed and agility events.[151] Burr calories reduces mainly to long, continued, moderate exercise.

val" training style has evolved as the principal method, but great emphasis is needed upon its progressive requirement. It is an alternation of hard and easy work which gets gradually harder and harder, with progressively greater dosage.[152]

To bring about the most important changes, consistency in workouts—day by day and week by week—is most important; it must also be realized that intermittent games such as bowling, golf, quoits, or short "weekend" bursts of effort will not do the job.[136] In testing a famous national champion in bowling at our laboratory, he was found to be little different than the average unexercised man. People in positive calorie balance fatten little by little, and one-tenth of a pound of fat per day will add up to 36.5 pounds in a year. It requires about 4380 calories of work to burn a pound of fat. Assuming that, in a good-sized man, 2000 calories are required to maintain the basal metabolism, and the man eats 4000 calories per day of food, then minimal daily exercise must account for 2000 calories to balance. This requires 2 or 3 hours of movement per day.[153]

PARALLEL EFFECTS UPON THE CIRCULATORY-RESPIRATORY AND METABOLIC SYSTEMS

Parellel Effects of Physical Training Upon Peak O_2 Intake and Cholesterol in Blood Serum

Studies of improvements in middle-aged humans affecting the maximal oxygen intake and cholesterol, respectively, show the parallel nature of the reversals. This, to our knowledge, has not been shown before. In this experiment, four middle-aged adults were trained for $1\frac{1}{2}$ hours per day, 6 days per week, combining warm-up calisthenics, cross-country running, and handball. The work was very vigorous and led to improvements in lowered cholesterol in 25 weeks from an average of 342 to 252 mg percent (sig.) for the subjects (Golding-Cureton, 1961).[154, 155] Golding was able to repeat the experiment in 1962[156] with similar changes on thirty subjects of the same age range, reducing the subjects from 261 to 195 mg percent as an average.

Furthermore, it is interesting and almost amazing to see that improvements in activities of the endurance type (with forced breathing), which last for a minute or more, plot also in a parallel way with respect to slopes *when all units are standard score units* ($6 \times$ SD per 100). This is shown in Figure 14, which compares the improvement slopes of six middle-aged subjects with the slopes of maximal O_2 intake and cholesterol in the blood serum (both plotted in standard scores).

The implications are that if subjects are exercised long enough and hard enough to improve the maximal oxygen intake, the cholesterol will

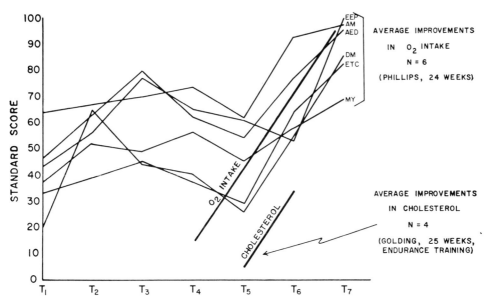

FIGURE 14. Parallel improvements of a peak O_2 intake and serum cholesterol. Same training program was used with both groups, $1\frac{1}{2}$ hours per day: calisthenics warm-up, cross-
country running, and handball (30 min each). Physical Fitness Research Laboratory, U.
of Ill.

reduce. Some programs of exercise do not reduce cholesterol significantly
because the work is too low in total kilocalorie cost.[136]

F. A. Kummerow, Professor of Animal Nutrition at the University of
Illinois and head of the University of Illinois Cholesterol and Lipids Chemistry Laboratory, has long noted the beneficial effects of exercise on adult
men in connection with our program; he has also personally participated
in it for about 15 years. Following is the diagram which he advanced to
indicate how cholesterol gets out of the body through the citric acid cycle
with by-products of *heat,* carbon dioxide, and water. Whereas, if this cycle
is not very active, any combination of fats, carbohydrates or proteins, in
combination with acetyl coenzyme A, will cause the accumulation of triglycerides and cholesterol in the body.

Our further generalization, backed by long experience, is that men do
not get fit by lying in hot rooms, or by being massaged on hot slabs. *The
heat must be generated by their own metabolism, by the use of their own
muscles.* Neither is it effective to have some machine or person do most of
the work while the subject passively submits.

Complicated Control of Circulation

The nervous control of circulation has been confirmed from a mass of
confused and sometimes conflicting data regarding the piecemeal approach,

Metabolic Fate of Carbohydrates, Fats and Proteins in Food*

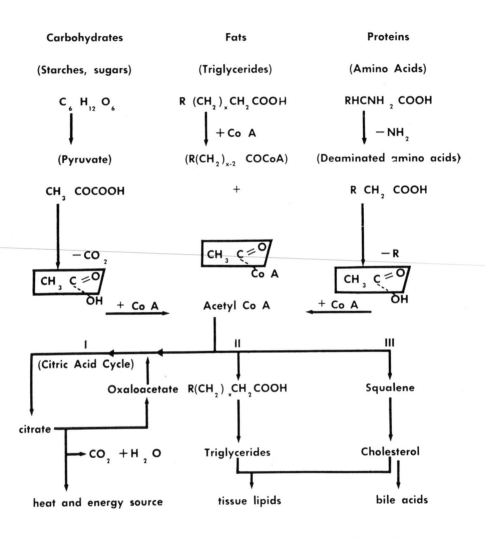

Carbohydrates	Fats	Proteins
(Starches, sugars)	(Triglycerides)	(Amino Acids)

DIAGRAM I. From Kummerow, F. A.: Illinois Med J, Nov. 1964.

*Digested food, partially metabolized is stored as glycogen, fat or tissue protein.

$CH_3 \, C{\scriptstyle=}^O$ — Acetyl group, a common building unit derived from all three major food components.

the conflict of the normal and the pathological, the vagus versus the sympatheticotonic, the stroke volume in different positions (lying, sitting, standing), and the relative value of the neuromuscular versus the circulatory point of view. The muscular movements make a good deal of the circulation day by day; but, for a time, the nervous system, because it has a kind of memory, will stimulate the heart and blood vessels to help circulation. However, in long periods of bed confinement, the circulation gradually decreases. The ambulatory program of the rehabilitation centers has adopted a policy of less and less bed rest to preserve the circulation (i.e., prevent deterioration).

Exercise creates strong somatic stimuli that go from the muscles in action to the spinal column, brain and hypothalamus, then to the heart, veins, arteries, and arteriolar sphincters. The circulation is affected very greatly by this complex regulatory nervous system. When the skin is constricted, the deeper organs may be better supplied, and vice versa. Staying in hot places too long may cause an unproportionate amount of blood to flow into the skin. Mental stimulus (a challenge) can stir up the sympathetic nervous system so that the heart stroke vigor is augmented at once, and further augmentation may come when the hormones from the medulla of the adrenals finally reach the heart tissues.

Uvnas[157] pointed up the role of the sympathetic nervous system by suggesting on the basis of his experiments that dilator fibers (sympathetic branches) dilate arterioles in the working muscles, and probably in the heart and lungs too. It is certain that exercise causes additional coronary circulation, as do alternate bouts of anoxia and forced breathing.[158, 159] It is even probable that such coronary dilation can be induced by just practicing breath holding and forced breathing at rest.[160] Gregg and Shipley[161] reported this sympathetic dilation of the coronaries as early as 1944. Such developments resulting from athletic training are viewed by Beckner and Windsor as normal physiological adaptations to secure greater stroke volume.

Sympatheticotonic changes brought on by cortical stimulation or by exercise are reflected in taller and sharper brachial pulse waves, a speeding of the intraventricular filling, and more contractile energy of the heart, which is typical of athletes in a high state of training. Brown, Bunnell and Greene[162] studied the shape of the brachial arterial pressure pulse curve. They found that when a Val Salva maneuver increased the intrathoracic pressure, all of the wave peaks became more prominent, especially the secondary diastolic wave. Norepinephrine infusion produced this same type of elevation. Amyl nitrite obliterated the secondary peak.

Eckstein and Abboud[163] studied the circulatory effects of sympatheticomimetic amines to show that epinephrine increased cardiac output and stroke volume and usually heart rate, but if the vagus tone is very strong, the first two can occur with a slowed pulse rate. A very strong vagus tone would slow the pulse rate. In fact, this combination is considered highly desirable because of the increased filling time of the heart, favorable to higher stroke output. The American Heart Association has recently advocated, following the research work of Dr. Carlos D. Mendez, accepting the faster intraventricular conduction velocity as helpful in assisting the heart to meet emergency efforts. Epinephrine delivered directly to the heart increased the rate and the strength of the heart contractions and shortened the time the heart muscle needed to recover before firing again (the refractory period).

Mendez proved that a substance from the liver under the influence of epinephrine caused the intraventricular speed-up, and that this was favorable to prevent fibrillation. The trend of these studies is to favor the development of a sympatheticotonic state in the heart muscle in preparation for a hard-working heart. This is just opposite to the older concept that a parasympathetic dominance is the natural state associated with athletic fitness.

Moreover, there were recent studies in the regulation of the heart by Sarnoff and Mitchell[164] of the Laboratory of Cardiovascular Physiology of the National Heart Institute at Bethesda. These studies of myocardial contractility (more external stroke work or power, and increased fiber tension during ejection of blood from the heart) proved that injection of epinephrine caused an immediate increased contractility of the heart myocardium. The ventricles normally eject whatever blood enters them, and force of ejection is greater from a greater diastolic end-volume in accordance with the Frank-Starling mechanism. With longer initial fiber length accompanying a greater inflow of blood into the ventricles, each ventricle will expel a greater stroke output on the beat-to-beat basis. With more myocardial tension, there may be greater amplitude of the systolic portion of the pressure pulse wave (more velocity); but, as Starr and his colleagues have shown, the velocity and acceleration measures are inversely related to age.[165]

Since potassium is essential to the work of the heart, and it enters the myocardial cell wall between contractions and leaves through the cell wall during contraction, the longer the rest-to-work time, the better are the conditions for this mechanism. Epinephrine was shown to be very helpful to increase the force and velocity of the heart stroke and to develop more work capacity of the heart muscle against the resistance, the efficient and capable heart responding more rapidly and with a larger stroke volume. Thus, the higher the level of the catecholamines present, like norepinephrine and adrenaline, the stronger the stroke. Cureton also demonstrated that limiting the supply of oxygen to the heart myocardium caused a loss of working capacity of the heart muscle (and less stroke volume and area under the pulse wave curve).

A number of authors have shown that direct stimulation of the isolated left stellate ganglion, with heart rate controlled by a pacemaker control apparatus, produced by such sympathetic stimulation a faster ejection of the blood from the heart and a faster relaxation after the peak of the ejection, commensurate with the trained heart capable of very hard work. This effect was present from any given end-diastolic pressure, whatever. Greater heart working capacity (ejection energy) was associated with greater efflux of catecholamine from the heart. Either the administration of the catecholamine or the stimulation of the sympathetic nerves supplying the ventricle produced a larger stroke, larger ejection wave, and greater working capacity of the heart. No effect on contraction was obtained by vagal stimulation.[166, 167, 168]

Several Swedish investigators (Uvnas and his associates) favor the view that the skeletal muscles, heart, and lungs can be affected by sympathetic fibers which dilate the small vessels and permit greater blood flow. The vasodilator effects are augmented by eserine and are blocked by atropine. Exercise warms up these small vessels, as it is a sympathetic stimulus, and there is more blood flow. These vasodilator neurons have their origin in the structures themselves and are not identical with the vasodilator reflexes. Whenever a sudden increase in blood flow is needed, at rest or in work, the mind stimulates the sympathetic nervous system, and the sympathetic outflow dilates the small blood vessels to reduce the peripheral resistance and to permit better blood flow; it also stimulates the pulsatile movements in the venous blood as well. But the action is both through (1) inhibiting the vasoconstrictor action in the small arterioles and capillaries and (2) inducing vasodilator activity in the critical places in the systemic circuit, that is, at the sphincter "sluice gates" at the end of the arterioles before they pass blood into the capillary beds.[169] Vascular tone results from a balance in these mechanisms. Several authors now support this theory, including Lindgren and Uvnas and Eliasson, Lindgren and Uvnas. Certain authors, Daggett *et al.*, have shown in dogs that vagal stimulation increases ventricular contractility and coronary blood flow.[170]

Recent researches on the pre-ejection heart intervals (Fig. 12) show that the TP interval may be shortened in progressively harder and harder programs, which are usually used in short-term athletic training.[171, 172, 173] There is some danger in such pressure programs for adults.[174] Sudden, intensive, oxygen-debt-inducing programs should be generally avoided, and the moderate, rhythmic programs of an aerobic nature should be allowed to dominate the training. After gradual progression, there may be some anaerobic work.

Rodbard[175] demonstrated that the normal interval from the onset of the QRS complex in the ECG to the first major deflection in the first heart-sound complex varies with stroke volume, and is normally 0.210 seconds. It shortens with exercise usually to about 0.130 seconds, and it returns to normal in approximately 10 minutes. The ICP interval has been advocated as more sensitive as an indicator of adrenosympathetic stimulation. The augmentor action of the sympathetic nerves to increase the "vigor of ejection" of the heart stroke has been substantiated by Randall and Rohse.[176]

VARIOUS EFFECTS OF GROUP TRAINING PROGRAMS

Phillips-Cureton Experiment with Middle-aged Subjects

A strenuous training program was carried out with six middle-aged subjects on a basis of training for 8 weeks, de-training for 8 weeks, and retraining for 8 weeks at the University of Illinois.[177] Seventy tests and measurements were taken once each month on the experimental subjects and on the four controls. The initial 8 weeks work was gradually progressive, composed of an initial 30-minute period of warm-up calisthenics, followed immediately by a 30-minute cross-country run (with some walking at first), and then 30 minutes of handball. After 8 weeks, the program was discontinued and men reverted to normal sedentary life. The subjects remained inactive for the second 8-week period, in which they performed the usual minimal activities of life. Then in a third 8-week period, the subjects were put back into training on a program somewhat longer and harder than they had followed in the first 8 weeks.

The results showed impressive changes in fat, moderate changes in weight, specific gravity, and vital capacity. The most impressive changes were in circulatory-respiratory and metabolic measures. Most important of all, perhaps, were the reductions in cholesterol in the blood serum. It had long been known that cholesterol did not reduce easily without changing the diet. The men ate whatever they liked throughout the experiment.

In general, there were improvements in all measures during the first few weeks, but, in general, the improvements were relatively greater in the last 8 weeks. Significant changes are shown (Fig. 15) in the brachial pulse wave, highest precordial R-wave of the ECG, the basal metabolic rate, and highest precordial T-wave of the ECG. Figure 16 shows the total serum cholesterol heart output per unit of size (proportional to the amplitude of the brachial pulse wave from the Michael-Cureton line chart), total peripheral resistance, and heart volume (Ungerleider-Clark tables).

From the results of this experiment, it appears that exercise of the continuous, rhythmical type, lasting 1 to $1\frac{1}{2}$ hours per day, is adequate to bring about important changes, but such changes are not obtained from more casually conducted programs or weekend programs. There are many trivial programs which do not work, especially those based upon a few seconds of "isometric" tensing-type exercises. Even golf, bowling, and volleyball have been shown to produce insignificant changes, and this has been usually true of the Canadian 5 BX and 10 BX programs.[178-181]

TABLE VI

CHANGES IN SIX MIDDLE-AGED MEN RESULTING FROM SIXTEEN WEEKS OF HARD PHYSICAL TRAINING

Experimental Subjects	Units	M.Y. (exp.)	E.E.P. (exp.)	A.E.D. (exp.)	A.M. (exp.)	D.M. (exp.)	E.T.C. (exp.)
Age	yrs	32	28	29	28	40	46
Weight	lbs	173.8 to 156.5	203 to 175	186.8 to 168.5	187.4 to 171.5	197.3 to 190.2	180 to 170.2
O_2 Intake (gross)	liters/min	1.71 to 2.58	2.56 to 4.41	2.46 to 4.03	3.21 to 4.58	1.504 to 4.43	1.89 to 3.59
Systolic amp. of heartograph	cm	0.95 to 1.34	1.00 to 2.35	0.90 to 1.54	1.04 to 1.78	0.75 to 1.30	0.94 to 1.16
Gross O_2 intake	cc/min/kg	24.6 to 40.0	27.8 to 59.8	29.1 to 52.8	37.7 to 53.8	16.8 to 48.2	22.9 to 46.4
Treadmill run	min	1:49 to 4:30	2:01 to 12:34	1:36 to 6:03	2:27 to 7:24	1:34 to 4:30	1:15 to 3:10
Basal metabolism rate	%	−6.84 to −4.81	−29.6 to +5.57	−26.8 to +3.1	−6.84 to −4.81	−26.8 to +3.1	−28.6 to +5.57
Terminal blood pressure of all-out treadmill run	mm Hg	226/90 to 232/84	200/102 to 186/50	260/94 to 220/70	184/90 to 196/94	184/90 to 196/94	176/86 to 200/100
Five-min. step test	beats	158 to 96	210 to 115	187 to 123	196 to 121	207 to 171	171 to 121
Mile run	min sec	7:30 to 6:17	6:39 to 4:58	7:07 to 6:04	6:10 to 5:14.2	8:37 to 6:35	7:37 to 6:38
Specific gravity		1.06924 to 1.09502	1.04923 to 1.08445		1.05124 to 1.08346	1.04237 to 1.06428	1.03564 to 1.05006
Total fat	mm	138 to 79	165 to 107	139 to 107	160 to 107	149 to 110	158 to 109
Body fat	%	18.5 to 6.3	28.4 to 11.2		27.4 to 11.7	31.8 to 20.9	35.3 to 28.0
Cholesterol (total serum)	mg%	325 to 200	270 to 175	220 to 165	285 to 180	285 to 210	405 to 240
Pulse rate—lying	beats/min	54 to 52	50 to 38	50 to 44	62 to 50	56 to 52	40 to 42
Blood pressures—lying	mm Hg	116/94 to 122/80	114/90 to 118/76	103/78 to 104/60	122/86 to 116/76	118/82 to 112/74	100/84 to 122/78
Total peripheral resistance	mg Hg cc/beat × sec	2.76 to 2.20	2.62 to 1.61	2.78 to 2.12	2.89 to 1.70	4.52 to 2.11	4.52 to 3.48

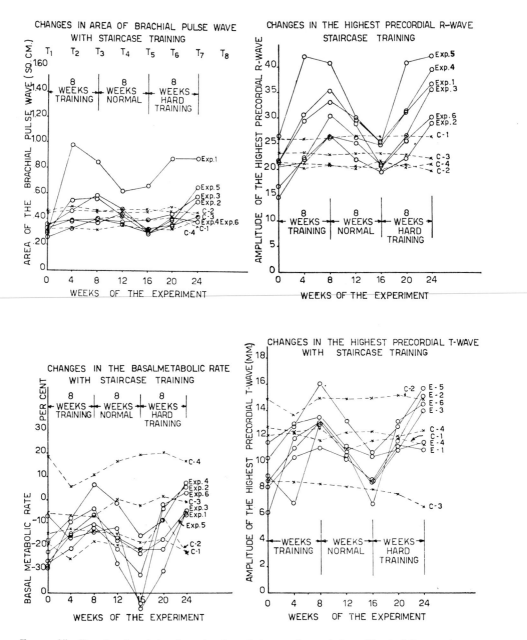

FIGURE 15. Results of training 8 weeks, de-training, and retraining. Physical fitness changes with 24 weeks of progressive exercise (calisthenics, running, and handball, 6 days per week), showing effects upon the brachial pulse wave, the precordial R-waves and T-waves of the ECG, and basal metabolic rate.

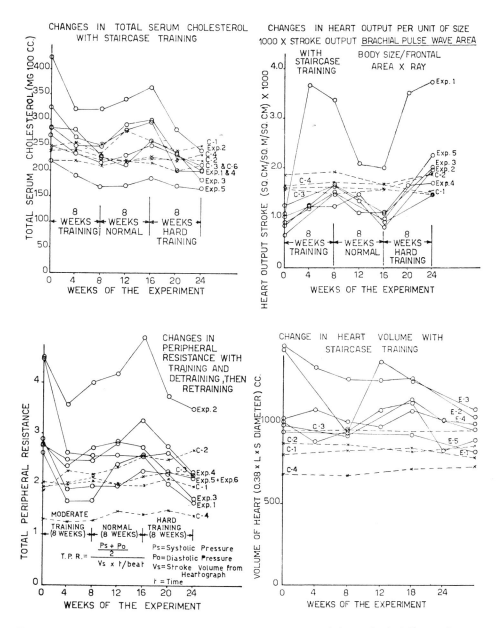

FIGURE 16. Results of training 8 weeks, de-training, and retraining. Physical fitness changes with 24 weeks total (calisthenics, running, and handball, 6 days per week), showing effects upon total serum cholesterol, heart output (by the Brachial Sphygmogram Method), and peripheral resistance. (Cureton-Phillips, *Med. Sportira.*)

Greater changes, relatively, were observed during the first 8 weeks of training, which was somewhat longer and harder, than in the second 8 weeks.

It is probable that because of the increased metabolic rate, the greater circulation in the quiet state, signs throughout of sympathetic tuning, and the associated stir-up of adrenergic hormones, that "trimming" was to be expected and even a significant effect upon circulating fats and the fat in depots.

Michael-Cureton Training Experiment, Ground Level and Altitude

Michael and Cureton made a training experiment upon three adult graduate students who were tested for cardiac output, stroke volume, and pulse rate every month during 12 weeks of progressive physical training; they then were followed as they de-trained gradually for 8 weeks more. The training consisted of track work, five times per week for approximately an hour on an indoor armory track. The work was one-half mile of warm-up or more, then an 880-yard run was repeated; finally, after 10 minutes of walking, there were two 220-yard sprints with 5 minutes of walking between. As the time went along week by week, an effort was made to improve the times. Physiological tests were given at "ground level" (altitude 240 feet) and also at a simulated altitude of 10,000 feet in a decompression chamber. The main purpose was to discover if such a track-training program would improve the tolerance to altitude stress, that is, could the men be trained to resist the stress without repeated exposures to altitude, or was oxygen deprivation due to the running program sufficient?

The Grollman method of testing stroke volume was used (method as modified by McMichael,[182] Christensen,[183] and with advice from Drs. Grollman and Asmussen). Reliability was finally accomplished after much work, the retest coefficients ranging from 0.88 to 0.90. Standard errors determined from retests are given in the original paper.[184]

Amplitude and area measurements taken of the brachial pulse wave were also essentially parallel to the stroke volume. The CFF (Critical Flicker Fusion Threshold) also paralleled the stroke volume. As training proceeded, after the first month systolic blood pressure, stroke volume, and pulse pressure went up for the 12 weeks of progressive training and retrogressed with gradual de-training. Figures 17 and 18 indicate some of the results of this experiment, and other diagrams are in the original article.

The stroke volume results showed that in the *first 4 weeks*, the training had an effect to decrease the stroke volumes, from 59 to 58 cc per beat at ground level and from 57 to 56 at simulated altitude. The apparent opposite reaction of stroke volume to minute volume (which increased) is explained by the fact that the pulse rate decreased during the first month while O_2 intake increased. The stroke volume *decreased* in all subjects in

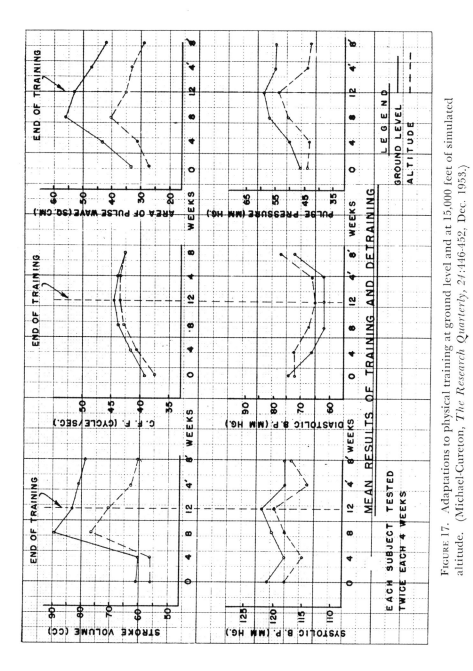

FIGURE 17. Adaptations to physical training at ground level and at 15,000 feet of simulated altitude. (Michael-Cureton, *The Research Quarterly, 24*:446-452, Dec. 1953.)

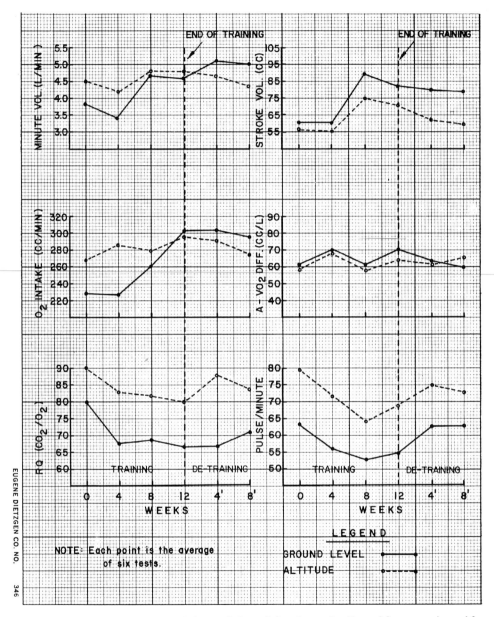

FIGURE 18. Mean changes in training and de-training in track. Repetitious running with gradual increase in work (Michael-Cureton).

going from ground level to simulated altitude in 15 minutes, but the minute volume increased. The decerase in stroke volume was paralleled by decreases in the T-wave of the highest precordial lead in the ECG and also by similar decreases in amplitude of the brachial pulse wave taken with the Cameron heartometer. Such depressions in vertical amplitude indicate oxygen shortage.

Other experiments in the literature have shown that the stroke volume determined by the Grollman acetylene method and also by the heartometer method gives values too low.[185] This is readily acknowledged, and Cureton made an age-slope comparison with data by Brandfonbrener and others to estimate the difference at the 20-to-25-year age span at 38 cc per beat.[186] Such a constant correction does not affect correlational relationships or the relative changes given in this study.

In the *second month,* the stroke volume in the ground level tests rose from 58 to 87 cc per beat, and the stroke volume was the highest when the pulse rate was the lowest; correspondingly, at simulated altitude, it rose from 56 to 75. The entire improvement was in the first 8 weeks, a gain of 36.6 percent at ground level (t = 2.11) and of 26 percent for the 15,000-feet simulated altitude test (t = 2.07), respectively. The average fluctuation in these stroke volume measurements was 12 percent, calculated from retests. (Table of errors is given in the original published report: *Res Quart, 24*: 446-452, Dec. 1953.) The RQ was the lowest at the end of the 12 weeks of training, leveled off during the next 8 weeks, after which it rose in both the ground level and altitude tests. Lowered RQ and lowered pulse rate were essentially parallel. The amplitude and area of the brachial pulse wave (taken with the Cameron heartometer) fell a bit in the altitude tests after training. The interpretation was that the training had adapted the nervous system to stand the stress better, so that there was no longer an "overshoot" because of the stress. The apparent effect of the same stress appeared to be less.

This experiment demonstrated that the training at ground level apparently toughened the nervous system so that the effect of the same stress was less and less as the time went on, and became least of all in the last 2 weeks. There was definite habituation (adaptation) to the stress by the development of what Dr. Hans Selye has termed a *general resistance.*[187]

In the ground-level tests, the O_2 intake test improved 30.3 percent (t = 2.19), the improvement being from 2.26 to 3.00 liters per minute in the first month, then decreased very slightly to 2.25 liters per minute in the second month of training, and rose sharply to 3.30 liters per minute in the third month of training. Since the subjects were quite fit to begin with, there was no significant weight change during the training.

In the simulated altitude tests during the first month, the O_2 intake rose from 2.68 to 2.88 liters per minute, leveled off, and then decreased sharply after the twelfth week to 2.76 liters per minute.

In the first month of training, the pulse rate decreased for all three subjects but increased as the training became harder, both at ground level and at simulated altitude. This indicated that this type of progressive training (repetitious bouts of increasing speed) induced a moderate sympatheticotonic effect. Before training at T_1 the pulse rate rose 17 beats, from 63 to 90 as an average, in changing from ground level to 15,000 feet of simulated altitude; but after training for 8 weeks, the pulse rate rose from 68 to 82, a difference of 14 beats; and after 12 weeks rose only 12 beats. The smaller increase in pulse rates indicates that the relative effect of the same stress was less after training. Thus, an *adaptation* to the stress had resulted. Such adaptation has been documented in the literature not only in oxygen economy but to heat, cold, and irradiation.[188]

Cureton-Pohndorf Swimming Training of Middle-aged Men

Two groups of middle-aged men were trained 50 minutes per day, followed by the administration of wheat germ oil in capsules and lard placebos, in an experiment at the University of Illinois conducted by Cureton and Pohndorf.[189]. The two matched groups of men, in age and all-out endurance on the treadmill, were trained in mixed-calisthenics (20 minutes) plus 30 minutes of endurance swimming in the pool. The work was rather hard, and the men were worked almost continuously during this time of 50 minutes, 5 days per week. A subproblem was to show any possible differences in the two matched groups which might have been due to the dietary supplement of wheat germ oil used. The men improved rather remarkably in the all-out treadmill run and in the several cardiovascular parameters. The (WGO) wheat germ oil group improved more than the group on devitaminized placebos. Since several other experiments have resulted in similar improvements and also advantages for the wheat germ oil and its derivative crystal (concentrate) form, octacosanol, it may be taken that the additional endurance and improved cardiovascular condition due to the dietary supplements are real.[190, 191, 192] The effect of such supplementation seems unusually indicated for work with middle-aged men who face stress day by day in physical training work.

In the graphs shown below, the experimental groups are shown as black bars in the center, with (left T_1 to T_2) WGO supplementation and without (T_1 to T_2). The effect of the exercise workouts plus the WGO supplements had an advantage over the group on the same exercises and placebos; in fact, the difference seems to be larger than the effect of WGO on subjects not taking the training exercises. It is probable that the exercises aid in the utilization of the oil, which otherwise may be wasted. Research dentists have

TABLE VII

EFFECT OF WHEAT GERM OIL SUPPLEMENT ON THE TREADMILL RUN

N	Group		Avg. Age	T_1 Avg. Raw Score	SS	T_2 Avg. Raw Score	SS	D Avg. Raw Score	D SS	Criterion 5% Level Sig.	Obtained Group Sig.
8	A	Ex. plus WGO	41.4	3.44	51.4	5.14	69.4	1.70	18.0	2.04	8.71
8	B	Ex. plus placebos	36.5	3.34	50.5	4.06	58.0	0.72	7.5	2.04	3.63
5	C	Inactive plus WGO	36.2	1.90	45.0	2.00	47.6	0.10	2.6	2.04	1.00
5	D	Inactive plus placebos	32.0	2.05	47.4	2.05	48.4	0	1.0	2.04	0

spoken of this "extra effect" as the third dimension of nutrition. Taking the oil immediately after the workouts seems to guarantee its utilization.

The findings of this study bear interest because important changes in endurance are paralleled by improvements in several types of cardiovascular tests. A condensation of the results follows:

Treadmill Run Results. Figure 19 shows that the WGO actively exercised group (Exp.) composed of eight men averaging 41.4 years of age improved from 3.44 to 5.14 minutes or 51.5 percent (18.0 SS %) on the all-out treadmill run test. The comparable group (controls) on lard placebos improved from 3.34 to 4.06 minutes, these men averaging 36.5 years of age (matched on treadmill run time). Both of these groups made a statistically significant change ($t_{exp.}$ = 8.71) and ($t_{con.}$ = 3.63). These two groups were also significantly different from each other in the gains made in running time ($t_{exp. vs con.}$ = 3.59).

The five inactive controls on WGO improved from 1.90 to 2.0 minutes, an insignificant gain (t = 1.0); also, the five inactive controls on placebos failed to gain (2.05 min to 2.05 min). The exercised group on WGO differed significantly from the control group which remained inactive but took WGO (t = 1.95). The changes are shown graphically in Figures 19 and 20.

Cardiovascular Changes. The systolic amplitude of the brachial pulse wave improved in a very similar way, practically paralleling the endurance results. In this measure the exercised WGO group gained from 1.32 to 1.76 cm, a raw-score gain of 33.5 percent (16.9 SS %). This was a statistically significant change better than the 1 percent level (t = 3.20). The exercised group on placebos gained from 1.35 to 1.39 cm, a gain of 2.96 percent (2 SS %), an insignificant gain (t = 0.33). The inactive WGO group gained from 1.41 to 1.47 cm or 4.26 percent (3 SS %), an insignificant change (t = 1.60).

In the area of the brachial pulse wave, the exercised group on WGO improved from 0.359 to 0.400 sq cm, while the inactive group *lost* from 0.349 to 0.299 sq cm. There was no significant difference between the inactive group on placebos and the exercised group on placebos (t = 1.60), but the exercised group improved from 0.359 to 0.400 sq cm, while the inactive group *lost* from 0.349 to 0.299. The trend here is to favor the WGO group. The brachial pulse wave test is a "naive" test, quite influenced by willpower. It is most interesting to see how the results paralleled the results of the all-out treadmill run test.

This entire experiment was repeated in another year with a new sample of middle-aged men; otherwise, all tests and conditions were the same. The results were similar. More complete details can be found in the original report.

Cureton-Wolf-Harrison Training Experiment

A swimming experiment was conducted at the Physical Fitness Research Laboratory using fifteen middle-aged men, 26 to 60 years of age, who took a swimming course led by a competent instructor, 5 days per week, for 6 weeks in the summer session.[193] The results are shown in Table VIII. There were statistically significant differences in the sitting brachial pulse wave, pulse rate, 5-Minute Harvard Step Test, basal metabolic rate, and fat.

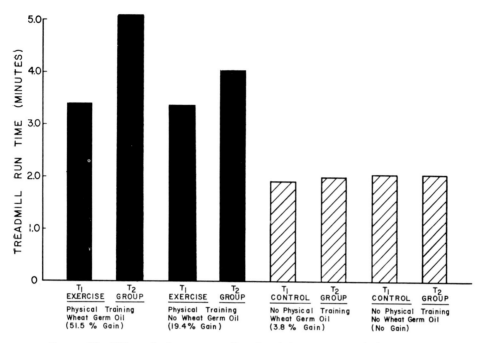

FIGURE 19. Effect of wheat germ oil and training upon treadmill running.

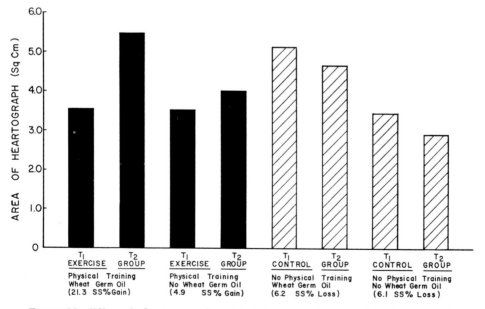

FIGURE 20. Effect of wheat germ oil and training upon the area of the heartograph.

The work in the swimming pool was preceded by a 10-minute land drill warm-up; then for 40 minutes, drills back and forth across the pool were called in alternate squads (1's and 2's) for 20 minutes; following that, the men swam lengths, but in two large circles usually to permit all to work at once.

TABLE VIII

IMPROVEMENTS IN MIDDLE-AGED MEN SWIMMING FOR ENDURANCE 6 WEEKS, FIVE DAYS PER WEEK

[Raw scores are converted to SS (standard scores) by table]

Fitness Test Items	Units	June, 1950 T' Mean	August, 1950 T_2 Mean	Improvement (D)	SD (σ) Diff.	D/σ Diff.
Cardiovascular						
1. Heartograph area	sq cm	43.71 SS	67.43 SS	24 SS	10.18	2.33
2. Systolic pulse wave amplitude	cm	57.43 SS	76.00 SS	19 SS	11.64	1.60
3. Diastolic pulse wave amplitude	cm	52.58 SS	72.28 SS	20 SS	10.53	1.90
4. Sitting pulse rate	beats --- min	54.57 SS	68.57 SS	14 SS	5.77	2.47
5. Schneider index	units	56.00 SS	64.00 SS	8 SS	8.78	.92
6. 5-Min Step Test (Brouha)	beats	32.62 SS	54.50 SS	22 SS	7.94	2.76
7. Barach index	units	180.88 SS	141.10 SS	19 SS	19.97	1.99
8. Standing pulse rate	beats --- min	50.30 SS	71.40 SS	21 SS	5.42	3.56
Respiratory						
9. Basal metabolic rate	Cal/hr /sq m	−21.9%	−14.2%	7%	3.82	2.02
10. Breath holding after 2 min step-up 30/min	sec	14.9 SS	15.3 SS	4.0 SS	2.31	.173
11. Normal breath holding	sec	72.9 SS	80.9 SS	8.0 SS	8.90	.90
(12-18 eliminated)						
Physique						
19. Total fat (sum of 6)	mm	154.3 SS	145.2 SS	5.0 SS	3.78	2.42
20. Weighted fat index	lbs	231.6 SS	216.9 SS	5.0 SS	4.47	3.28

Note: Forty-two other items were dropped because of low significance. These included the blood pressure items, the separate strength items, vital capacity, the ECG vertical deflections, the skeletal index, and the muscular girth index.

Skinner-Holloszy-Cureton Experiments on Middle-aged Men

In collaboration with the U. S. Public Health Service, an experiment was conducted on middle-aged men, four of whom were coronary suspects because of not meeting the standards of the Master Two-step Test, and one of whom was a postcoronary subject.[194] Since the experiment has been published in the *American Journal of Cardiology* in full, the details are not repeated here. It may be of interest that this experiment produced impressive improvements; the heart-diseased subject and the suspects caught up with the normal men in 5 months of gradual progressive exercise of the rhythmic, forced-breathing type which has long been used by Cureton[195] with middle-aged men. The program was begun very gradually; after the fourth month, it was pushed up from about 200 kilocalories daily to 300; in the fifth month, it was still further increased to approximately 400 kilocalories per day. The men were 35 to 55 years of age. No changes were made in diet.

The results showed steady progression in work capacity on a bicycle ergometer test (to 150 pulse rate maximum) from October to April. Specific gravity was increased significantly, and fat was reduced. Weight stayed the same (175.6 to 175.7 lbs). Heart force, as measured on the ultralow frequency BCG, improved significantly in all subjects. The serum triglycerides fell from 208 to 125 mg percent in a significant reduction, but the group mean of cholesterol and phospholipids did not decrease significantly. However, two men had weight losses and also significant reductions in cholesterol.

Pohndorf's Experiment on Two Middle-aged Subjects

R. H. Pohndorf[196] completed a study on a middle-aged doctor and his wife, also a physician. The subjects were instructed to swim 1000 yards per day for 5 months. In trying to cut down the time required for the workouts, the cholesterol which had lowered from 260 mg percent to 190 on the 45 minutes per day of continuous swimming began to go up again. The training was stopped, and the cholesterol went back to its previous high level. All through the next winter it stayed up; in the spring, the swimming was begun on 1000 yards per day dosage, and the cholesterol was again lowered. The changes in the wife were similar but not as great as for the husband.

Ribisl-Cureton Training Experiment

Fifteen men, averaging 40.2 years of age (33 to 48) were run over a cross-country course at the University of Illinois for 5 months, four or five times per week. The total distance was 3.5 miles. At the beginning of the experiment, most of them could not run more than a mile, but all improved impressively. In the 2-mile run for time given after the first 2 months, the improvement was from 17:42 to 14:41.5, an average reduction in time of approximately 3 minutes. Concomitantly, the improvement in "peak" oxygen intake (from 40.12 to 45 ml/kg/min) showed a statistically significant difference greater than the .01 level. Other significant changes were in maximum pulmonary ventilation (13.9 liters/min) and in maximal oxygen pulse (2.13 ml/beat). Each of these measures normally declines with advancing age, so that the improvements may be interpreted as "reversing the age trend" (Fig. 21).[197]

The reference line in solid in the center is from Robinson's work published in 1938 (in cc/min/kg), the upper and lower dotted lines showing the values in liters per minute for maximal work (top line) in the treadmill run, 8.6 percent grade and the values for walking 5.6 mph on the horizontal grade.

It is most impressive to see the improvements in oxygen intake in middle-aged men, but it only verifies what has been known to be true, i.e., that there is a high relationship between the endurance runs of a mile or more and the aerobic oxygen intake "peak" capacity. It appears that the longer the run, the higher the relationship is, because the "steady state" is developed and the men run without developing an oxygen debt, except probably at the finish if they sprint for the finish line.

Moreover, if the age-slope line is drawn through the top of the improvements in a mean fit, then the line would extend to the base line at approxi-

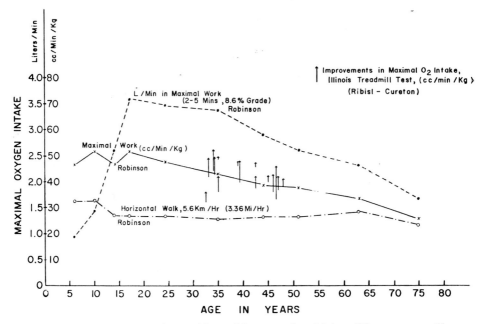

FIGURE 21. Improvements in aerobic working capacity. Males, different ages. (From Robinson, Sid: Experimental studies of physical fitness in relation to age. *Arbeitsphysiologie, 10*:251, 1938.)

mately 120 years. Of course, no men in a group have been followed who have run all of their lives, or at least as long as they possibly could. Perhaps someday we may know what this would produce since there are many long-distance runners over 75 years of age who are still running.

VARIOUS EFFECTS OF INDIVIDUALIZED TRAINING PROGRAMS

Example One—Mixed Program of Walking, Calisthenics, Running, and Swimming

Another subject (R.L.) was 46 years of age, a male insurance executive. Thirty years before, he had been a high-school diver, and he came into the fitness program for adults feeling that he had deteriorated far below his 16- to 20-year status. He felt very tired nearly all of the time, complained of several chronic ailments, and had put on 25 pounds since his graduation from high school. Feeling his loss of fitness severely, especially the fatigue, fatness, tension, and slowing up of his sex life, he volunteered to take 6 months off from his work to participate in an experimental program. He said that in his opinion many insurance executives had the same problem. It was his proposition that if the progressive exercise program produced good results in his case, he would see that insurance executives from various companies would know about it in due time. This actually resulted, so this case is of great interest.[198]

He began with a daily walking program, increasing this progressively from 1, to 2, to 3, to 4, and to 5 miles per day in the first month. The program tired him so much that he worked only three times per week and went home to Chicago on the weekends. Then, after the first month, he worked every day, 5 days per week, adding heel-toe walking, flat-foot jogging, and swimming. At the end of 2 months, he was accomplishing about 200 kilocalories of work per day, 5 days per week. During the third month, he increased this to 300 kilocalories per day; in the fourth month to approximately 400, working twice per day; and in the fifth and sixth months, he worked very hard, about 500 to 600 per day, working twice per day doing walking, calisthenics, running, and swimming.

The results were gratifying in the way he felt. He doubled the time he could run on the treadmill at 5 mph and progressed to 7 mph. There were marked improvements in vital capacity and breath holding after 1 minute of exercise. There were marked improvements in the vigor of his heart stroke and in all cardiovascular tests, especially basal metabolism (without any drugs). His weight dropped 13 pounds, and his fat from 179 mm to 139.5 mm (sum of 6 fat folds test). The difference between his maximum chest expansion and normal abdominal girth increased from 6.0 to 9.6 (87 SS). His heart size reduced from +5.5 to −2.56 percent (Ungerleider-Clark

Tables), equivalent to 15 SS reduction, and his heart rate and blood pressures were much lower on the standard 4-minute jog, 5 miles per hour (8.6% grade on the motor-driven treadmill). His average progressive pulse ratio dropped from 2.47 to 2.14, and the "break in the plotted line" which indicated a quickly developed oxygen debt was virtually eliminated with obviously better endurance. His results are summarized in Table IX.

Results of this kind have caused us to do more and more of this work. The use of the dynamic health (exercise) procedures has spread rapidly in

TABLE IX

IMPROVEMENT OF A MIDDLE-AGED SUBJECT
BY RHYTHMIC RUNNING AND SWIMMING

Subject: R. L. (No. 61) Test Items	*Units*	*Age 49-6* T'		*Age 50* T₂		*Ht. 71.0* Gain
Treadmill run	min and					
5 mph	sec	2:07	(37)	4:00	(53)	16
Vital capacity residual	cu in	6	(58)	41	(75)	17
Breath holding after						
1 min exercise	sec	14	(45)	16	(47)	2
2 min exercise	sec	13	(22)	25	(39)	17
Cardiovascular Tests:						
Brachial pulse wave/SA		.219	(65)	.363	(105)	40
Standing sys. BP	mm Hg	118	(55)	112	(63)	8
Standing dias. BP	mm Hg	100	(21)	80	(54)	2
Heartograph sys. amp.	cm	1.50	(59)	2.37	(125)	66
Pulse rate (sitting)	beats/min	64.6	(67)	62.8	(73)	6
Schneider index	score	12	(55)	15	(68)	13
5' Step test	beats	176	(28)	140	(89)	61
Barach index	score	191.8	(22)	181	(39)	17
Gale BMR	%	−1.0	(44)	+11	(56)	12
BMR (basal O₂)	%	−18.8	(35)	−11.04	(43)	8
Avg PP ratio	score	2.47	(42)	2.14	(65)	23
Area brachial pulse wave	sq cm	2.50		4.96		
Area frontal x-ray	sq cm	180		141.1		
ECG (Tiv-v wave)	mm	9.9		11.6		
Total O₂ in jog	L	10.29	(38)	12.13	(46)	8
Post-ex BP	mm Hg	207/86		170/78		
Physique Tests:						
Fat	mm	179	(32)	139.5	(58)	26
Vital capacity residual	cu in	+6	(58)	+41	(75)	17
Chest expansion	in	4.5	(85)	5.5	(112)	27
Exp. chest girth—ab. girth	in	6.0	(61)	9.6	(87)	26
Heart size	%	5.5	(58)	−2.56	(43)	−15
Weight	lbs	183.8	(74)	170.8	(65)	9

Note: Figures in parentheses are standard score values, based upon 6 sigma spread; these are necessary to compare the relative gain on the tests.

the executive group of insurance men. There are very marked extensions of *predicted* length of life from Kellogg's Blood Pressure (Loss of Life) Tables,[199] associated with such reductions in blood pressures and peripheral resistance.

Example Two

Figure 22 shows a middle-aged man's profile chart, showing his *before training* (dotted line) graph in the various measures of cardiovascular condition taken at rest. There are ten measures taken from the heartograph, measured with the Cameron Heartometer, which this laboratory has used for 16 years. This is only one part of a much larger picture, but there is no question that the subject has a lower pulse pressure, a much stronger stroke of the heart with more area, and a taller and sharper primary stroke

4/30/53   CHANGES IN THE HEARTOGRAPH

Subject: S.L.T.   (QUIET SITTING POSITION BEFORE EXERCISE)

7/31/53   (Graphs taken at 80mm Hg Pressure, sitting)

Classification	Area Under the Curve	Area/Surface Area	Systolic Amplitude	Diastolic Amplitude	Obliquity Angle	Rest to Work Ratio	Pulse Rate	Systolic Blood Press.	Diastolic Blood Press.	Pulse Pressure	Standard Scores	Percentile
AFTER	.78 [76]	.458	2.74	[1.58/1.38]	14.8	3.46	39	80	33	96	100	99.87
Excellent	.74	.433	2.61	1.30	15.5	3.28	43	84	37	[91/90]	95	99.65
TRAINING	.70	.408	2.48	1.24	16.1	3.10	46	88	41	87	90	99.18
	.66	[.390/.383]	2.35	1.16	16.8	[2.92/2.86]	[50]	92	44	82	85	98.2
Very Good	.62	.358	[2.22/2.17]	1.10	17.5	2.74	54	96	48	78	80	96.4
	.58	.333	2.09	1.02	18.2	2.56	58	100	52	[77/73]	75	93.3
	.54	.308	1.96	.96	18.8	[2.42/2.38]	61	104	55	68	70	88.4
Above Average (Good)	.50	.283	1.83	.88	[19.5/20.0]	2.20	65	108	59	64	65	81.6
	.46	.258	1.70	.82	20.2	2.02	69	112	63	59	60	72.6
	.42	.233	1.57	.74	20.8	1.84	73	116	66	55	55	61.8
Average	.38	.208	1.44	.68	21.4	1.66	[76/77]	120	70	50	50	50.0
	.34	.183	1.31	.60	22.0	1.48	80	124	74	46	45	38.2
	.30	.158	1.18	.54	22.8	1.30	84	128	[78/80]	41	40	27.4
Below Average (Fair)	.26 [.133/.127]		1.05	[.46/.43]	[23.5/24.0]	1.12	88	132	81	36	35	18.4
	.22	.108	.92	.40	24.2	.94	91	136	85	32	30	11.5
BEFORE	[.21].18	.083	[.87/.79]	.32	24.8	.76	95	140	[89/90]	27	25	6.7
Poor	.14	.058	.66	.26	25.5	.58	99	144	92	23	20	3.6
TRAINING	.10	.033	.53	.18	26.2	.40	103	148	96	18	15	1.8
	.06	.008	.40	.12	26.9	.22	106	152	100	14	10	.82
Very Poor	.02	0	.27	.04	27.5	.04	110	156	103	9	5	.35
	0	0	.14	0	28.2	0	114	[160/167/170]	107	4	.0	.14
Mean	.38	.208	1.44	.675	21.37	1.66	76.35	119.68	70.25	50.2		
Sigma	.147	.085	.44	.247	2.24	.61	12.5	12.36	12.30	15.24		
Number	281	256	288	272	263	260	319	438	438	438		
Range	.14-.99	.06-.56	.54-3.40	.13-1.65	15-31	.35-5.33	32-128	82-186	35-115	10-106		

FIGURE 22. Graphs show changes in a hypertensive subject in approximately 3 months of calisthenics (20 min) plus swimming (30 min), 5 days per week in a continuous nonstop program with ten capsules of whole, fresh Viobin wheat germ oil taken after each workout.

(smaller obliquity angle). The systolic amplitude is highly correlated with the *velocity* of the blood ejected from the heart and reflects a much greater *initial impulse*; the more acute obliquity angle reflects a greater relative acceleration of the primary stroke. This subject (S.L.T.) has been followed for 13 years, and he was in very poor condition, in the opinion of his doctor, when he began the program. In training, after 6 months on rhythmical endurance exercises and swimming, he manifested higher T-waves in the electrocardiogram and demonstrated much greater endurance in the pool. In de-training this reversed.

Example Three—Training Changes in Progressive Training in Swimming at the Competitive Level

The data from the study of W. W. Huesner,[200] completed as a thesis working with the writer and his laboratory staff, are shown in Table X. The subject (WWH) went through 1 month of de-training, 2 months of land drills, 2 months of pool drills, and 2 months of competition; he then de-trained again for 2 months. The data are shown in two states: (1) quiet resting state and (2) in hard work on an all-out treadmill run (with some measures taken as soon as possible, 1 minute to 1 minute and 15 seconds, after the cessation of the work). The subject was 26 years of age, a male graduate student in physical education, and a former Olympic swimmer for Northwestern University in the 1500 meter swim. He worked out 2 hours per day in his practice workouts, 6 days a week. The entire program was spread over 23 weeks with measurements taken every 4 weeks. His detailed training program may be found in his Ph. D. thesis.

His weight at the beginning was 186.8 pounds, and at the peak of training was 189.5, after which he went up to 193.0 after stopping the workouts in the last 2 months of de-training. His surface area was 2.08 up to 2.10 and after de-training 2.12 sq meters. Height remained constant at 73.4 inches. His chest increased in girth from 40 to 41.5 inches (expanded), while abdominal girth decreased from 33.1 to 32.2 during the training period. The tables of data include 256 test items covering a wide range of physique, circulatory-respiratory, and motor-test items, including the times on the 100-, 220-, and 440-yard swims every month. Total caliper fat began at 120 mm (total of 6 places) and ended at 93 mm at end of training: whereas the muscular girth index moved upward from 148.3 pounds. His weight residual went up from 34.1 to 39.4 pounds; buoyancy (time to rise 7 feet, Cureton Test) decreased from 7.0 to 9.4 seconds (0.9825 to 0.9865 in specific gravity, uncorrected for residual air in lungs); vital capacity increased from 369 to 387 cubic inches ($37°$ C); blood pH from 7.42 to 7.38 at rest before the test run, and 7.26 to 6.93 afterward. The heart volume by the Ungerleider-Clark Table reduced

TABLE X

PROGRESSIVE CHANGES IN THE PHYSICAL FITNESS
OF AN ADULT MALE
DURING A SEASON OF TRAINING FOR COMPETITIVE SWIMMING

Progression by Months	Gale (% BMR)	Basal TPR (mm Hg/cc × time/ beat)	Area/ SA (sq cm)	Systolic Amp. (cm)	Stroke Volume (cc/beat)	Sitting PR (beats/ min)	Rest/ Work (heart-ograph)	O₂ Intake (L/Min)	Net O₂ Intake (L/min /kg)	PP (1 min after) (mm Hg)	Net Total O₂ (L)	Stroke Volume (cc/beat)	Time of Run (min and sec)
				Resting State						*Hard Work (in, or immediately after)*			
1. De-trained	6	1.352	.178	1.21	60.3	72	1.53	1.78	.024	88	8.15	104.7	1:11
2. Land drills	4	1.180	.199	1.35	82.8	64	2.28	2.57	.030	106	8.34	127.2	1:13
3.	1	1.233	.191	1.43	80.3	64	2.40	2.77	.032	113	10.98	126.9	1:30
4. Pool drills	8	1.093*	.195	1.26	84.9*	72	2.81	3.21	.037	110	9.93	153.1	1:34
5.	6	1.262	.171	1.25	78.5	68	3.00*	3.10	.036	156	12.38	147.5	1:50
6. Competition	14	1.234	.213*	1.57*	69.1	64	2.28	3.90*	.041*	162*	14.47	176.2*	1:53
7.	15*	1.204	.200	1.40	82.3	72	2.23	3.70	.039	121	15.12*	163.5	2:00*
8. De-training	13	1.189	.185	1.45	72.9	68	2.13	3.78	.040	80	11.59	160.1	1:37
9.	7	1.226	.179	1.30	74.8	72	1.86	3.15	.032	104	10.42	130.7	1:25

*Peak score or performance.

in size from 0% to −2.6% and by the Keys-Friedel Equation from 989 cc to 815 cc. The basal metabolic rate went up from 38.4 to 43.1 Cal/hr/sq. m. (−2.79% to +9.12 by Aub-Dubois Standards).

The subject's 440-yard swim time improved in monthly trials from 5:14.7 to 4:44.6, the 100 yard from 56.2 to 51.8 seconds. Table X shows the principal changes in the cardiovascular data. It is shown that the stroke volume increased from 104.7 to 163.5 as the result of the training; this improvement was paralleled by an O_2 intake increase from 1.78 liters per minute to 3.70 (Cureton's 1-Bag Test, All-Out Treadmill Run, 8.6% grade, 10 mph), and the run time improved from 1.11 to 2.00 on the same test. The net O_2 intake (liters./min/kg) rose from 24 to 41, and the total O_2 from 8.15 to 15.12 liters. The best time corresponded in the all-out run to the peak stroke volume, the peak total O_2 and pulse pressure after the run test. Peak values in the systolic amplitude of the heartograph and area per square meter of surface were also at a peak in the month before the peak time and peak oxygen measures, with steady improvement in these measures on the heartometer. The heartometer stroke volume improved from 60.3 cc per beat to 82.3 cc per beat (from the Michael-Cureton line chart). Basal total peripheral resistance reduced from 1.352 to 1.204 mm Hg per cc × time per beat (Cureton's heartograph equation); and the corresponding to a reduction in volume elasticity (rigidity) of 1.890 to 0.972 from E (mm Hg per cc).

The stress of the training is indicated by the drop in pH and in hemoglobin (Hb) the latter from 37.0 to 29.6 (10^{-12} gm per erythrocyte), while the white blood count rose from 4300 to 7425. All of the muscular endurance tests increased during the training period.

This is one of the very few available records of progressive training followed in such detail. It seems clear that there is a progressive build-up in the working capacity, the oxygen intake capacity, and the swimming ability. These improvements are practically paralleled by the build-up in stroke volume, the heartograph area and systolic amplitude, basal metabolic rate and fat reduction—all of these measures reflecting the improved fitness of the subject.

References

62. WIGGERS, CARL J.: *Circulatory Dynamics.* New York, Grune, 1952, pp. 17-18.
63. RALSTON, H. J.; GUTTENTAG, O. E., and OGDEN, E.: *Proc Soc Exp Biol Med, 53*:154-156.
64. BRANDFONBRENER, M.; LANDOWNE, M., and SHOCK, N.: Changes in cardiac output with age. *Circulation, 12*:557-566, Oct. 1955.
65. CURETON, T. K.: Comparison of methods for determining cardiac output. *Phys Educ Today, 7*:15-20, March 1960.
66. BAINBRIDGE, F. A.: *The Physiology of Exercise.* New York, Longmans, Green and Co., 1923, pp. 87-88.

67. STARR, ISAAC: An essay on the strength of the heart and the effect of aging upon it. *Amer J Cardiol, 14* (No. 6, Symposium on Work and the Heart): 771-783, Dec. 1964.

68. FARHI, ASHER: Relative Statistical Contribution of Factors in Total Peripheral Resistance Formulas for Adult Men. Ph.D. Thesis, Physical Education, U. of Ill., 1966.

69. McADAM, R. E.: An Investigation of the Effects of Physical Training Upon the Cardiovascular Components. Ph.D. Thesis, Physical Education, U. of Ill., 1955.

70. CURETON, T. K.: Relationship of physical fitness to athletic performance and sports. *JAMA, 162*:1139-1151, Nov. 17, 1956.

71. CURETON, T. K.: The relative value of various exercise programs to protect adult human subjects from degenerative heart disease. In Raab, W. (Ed.): *Prevention of Ischemic Heart Disease.* Springfield, Thomas, 1966, p. 322.

72. PALLANDI, TAIMO: The Effects of Progressive Fitness Training on the Total Peripheral Resistance of Sedentary Adult Men. M. S. Thesis, Physical Education, U. of Ill., 1965.

73. RALSTON *et al., op. cit.*

74. WIGGERS, *op. cit.*

75. BRANDFONBRENER *et al., op. cit.*

76. MASUDA, MAKOTO: An analysis of human peripheral vascular resistance during exercise. *Bull Phys Fitness Res Inst, II*:17-23, March 1967.

77. ECKSTEIN, R. W.: Effect of exercise on the growth of coronary arterial anastomoses subsequent to coronary arterial narrowing in dogs. *Circulation, 14*:930, Nov. 1956.

78. RING, G. C.; BLUM, A. S., and KURBATOV, T.: Exercise and the minute vessels of the pulmonary circuit. *J Sport Med, 2*:27-30, March 1962.

79. JOKL, E.: Petrén on the effect of growth and training on the capillarization of the central nervous system. *Res Quart, 17*:127, May 1946.

80. OGAWA, Y.: A study of vascular pattern changes of muscular training. *XVI Weltkongress Fur Sportmedicin,* Hannover. 1966, pp. 765-768.

81. UVNAS, B.: Sympathetic vasodilator outflow. *Physiol Rev, 34*:608-618, July 1954.

82. KROGH, AUGUST: *The Anatomy and Physiology of the Capillaries.* New Haven, Yale, 1922, pp. 197, 199, 201.

83. OGAWA, *op. cit.*

84. BARCROFT, H., and SWAN, H. J. C.: *Sympathetic Control of Human Blood Vessels.* London, Arnold and Co., 1953, p. 9.

85. AVIADO, D. M., JR.; LING, J. S. L.; QUIMBY, C. W., JR., and SCHMIDT, C. F.: *Fed Proc, 13*:4-5, March 1954.

86. PETREN, T.; SJÖSTRAND, T., and SYLVAN, B.: Der Einfluss des Trainings aufdie Häufigkeit der Capillaren in Herz und Skelmuskulatur. *Arbeitsphysiologie, 9*:376, 1936.

87. UNGERLEIDER, H. E., and CLARK, C. P.: A study of the transverse diameter of the heart silhouette with prediction tables based on the teleoroentgenogram. *Amer Heart J, 17*:92, Jan. 1939. (Brochure of the Equitable Life Insurance Co.)

88. KEYS, ANCEL, and FRIEDEL, H. L.: Measurements of heart size with the roentgenkymograph. *Fed Proc, 4* (No. 1), March 1945; *Amer J Roentgen, 44*:805-33, Dec. 1940; *Proc Soc Exp Biol Med,* 40:267-70, 1939; and *Science, 88*:566-68, Nov. 11, 1938.

89. CURETON, T. K.: Measurements of heart size related to athletic performance. In

Physical Fitness of Champion Athletes. Urbana, U. of Ill., 1951, pp 105-136. Also the hearts of athletes. *Illinois Med J, 86*:143, June 1951.

90. CURETON, T. K.: The brachial pulse wave test of cardiovascular condition. In *Physical Fitness of Champion Athletes.* Urbana, U. of Ill., 1951, pp. 228-254. Also *Illinois Med J, 99*:143, 1951.

91. CURETON, T. K.: Shrinkage of heart size associated with improved cardiovascular condition due to progressive physical training of three middle-aged men. *J Phys Ment Rehab, 10*:75-88+, May-June 1956.

92. HERXHEIMER, H.: Zum Einfluss des Radfahrens auf die Herzgrosse. *Klin Wschr, 2*:1549, 1923. Also observations on the hearts of athletes. *Klin Wschr, 1*:2286, July-Dec. 1922, and *Klin Wschr, 5*:749, April 1926.

93. REINDELL, H.: Kymographische und Elektrokardiographische Befund am Sportherzen. *Deutsch Arch Klin Med, 131*:485-514, 1937.

94. WOLFFE, J. B., and DIGLIO, V. A.: The heart in the athlete. *J Health Phys Educ and Rec, 20*:8-9, 1949.

95. WOLFFE, J. B., and MUELLER, G. W.: The heart of the athlete. *Phys Educator, 6*:305, May 1949.

96. TANNER, LAURI: Some notes on medical research into athletics in Finland. Stockholm, *Kongressen* (Lingiad), 1949, II, pp. 192-196.

97. CURETON, T. K., and PHILLIPS, E. E.: Physical fitness changes in middle-aged men attributable to equal eight-weeks period of training, non-training and re-training. *J Sport Med, 4* (No. 2):87-93, June 1964.

98. HOLLOSZY, J. O.; SKINNER, J. S.; BARRY, A. J., and CURETON, T. K.: Effect of physical conditioning on cardiovascular function. *Amer J Cardiol* (Symposium Report), *14*:761-770, Dec. 1964.

99. HOLMGREN, A., *et al.*: Effect of training on work capacity, total Hb, blood volume, heart volume and pulse rate in recumbent and upright positions. *Acta Physiol Scand, 50*:72-83, 1960.

100. NAUGHTON, JOHN, and NAGLE, F.: Peak oxygen intake during physical fitness program for middle-aged men. *JAMA, 191*:103-105, March 15, 1965.

101. RIBISL, PAUL M.: Effects of training upon the maximal oxygen intake of middle-aged men. Ph.D. Thesis, Physical Education, U. of Ill., 1967.

102. GUALTIERE, WILLIAM S.: A comparative study of the effects of two training programs on Blood volume and cardiovascular-pulmonary functions. Ph.D. Thesis, Physical Education, U. of Ill., 1967.

103. CURETON, T. K.: The nature of cardiovascular fitness in humans. Part II. Hydrostatic drop. *J Phys Ment Rehab, 11*:186-196, Nov.-Dec. 1957.

104. GELLHORN, ERNST: *Autonomic Imbalance and the Hypothalamus.* Minneapolis, U. of Minn., 1957.

105. CURETON, T. K.: Effects of longitudinal physical training on the amplitude of the highest pre-cordial T-wave of the ECG. *Med Sport* (Roma), *12*:259-281, July, 1958. Also scientific control of training. *Phys Educ Today* (Manila), *7*:7-9, March 1960.

106. ROSE, K. D., and DUNN, F. L.: Physiology of Running Studied by Use of Radio Telemetry. Unpublished paper, Presented March 20, 1964, Hollywood, Meeting of the American College of Sports Medicine.

107. CARLISLE, FORBES: T-wave changes in the electrocardiogram associated with prolonger

periods of strenuous exercise in sportsmen with special reference to applications in trained swimmers. *Australian J Phys Educ,* Nov.-Dec. 1959.

108. CURETON, and PHILLIPS, *op. cit.*

109. CURETON, T. K., and DU TOIT, S. F.: Effect of progressive physical training on the latent period of electrical stimulation of the left ventricle of the human heart. *Proc. College Phys Educ Ass,* Dec. 27-29, 1965, pp. 121-122.

110. DU TOIT, STEPHANUS F.: Running and Weight Training Effects Upon the Cardiac Cycle. Ph.D. Thesis, Physical Education, U. of Ill., 1966.

111. CURETON and DU TOIT, *op. cit.*

112. GELLHORN, *op. cit.*

113. CARLISLE, FORBES: *Forbes Carlisle on Swimming.* London, Pelham Books, Ltd.

114. CURETON, T. K.: *Physical Fitness Appraisal and Guidance.* St. Louis, Mosby, 1947, pp. 559-560.

115. CURETON, T. K.: *Physical Fitness of Champion Athletes,* Appendix E. St. Louis, Mosby, 1947, p. 559.

116. ROSE, K. D., and DUNN, F. L.: Telemeter electrocardiography. *Nebraska Med J, 49*:447-56, Sept. 1964.

117. IBID.

118. HYMAN, A. S.: The Q-first heart sound interval in athletes at rest and after exercise. *J Sports Med, 4*:199-203, Dec. 1964.

119. RAAB, W.: Cardiac sympathetic tone and stress response related to personality patterns and exercise habits. In *Prevention of Ischemic Heart Disease.* Springfield, Thomas, 1966, pp. 121-134.

120. RAAB, W.: Training, physical inactivity and the cardiac dynamic cycle, (preventive aspects). *J Sports Med, 6*:38-47, March 1966.

121. RAAB, W.: Degenerative heart exercise from lack of exercise. In *Exercise and Fitness,* University of Illinois Colloquium. Chicago, Athletic Institute, 1960, p. 248.

122. SLONIGER, E. L.: The Relationship of Stress Indicators to Pre-Ejection Cardiac Intervals. Ph.D. Thesis, Physical Education, U. of Ill., 1966.

123. CURETON and DU TOIT, *op. cit.*

124. DONALD, D. E.: Exercise Capacity in Dogs with Cardiac Denervation. Mayo Clinic Convention paper. *Amer Physiol Soc,* unpublished report.

125. CURETON, T. K.: Sympathetic versus vagus influence upon the contractile vigor of the heart. *Res Quart, 32*:553-557, Dec. 1961.

126. CURETON, T. K.: Anatomical, physiological and psychological changes induced by exercise programs (exercises, sports, games) in adults. In *Exercise and Fitness,* University of Illinois Colloquium. Chicago, Athletic Institute, 1960, pp. 152-182. Also improvement of cardiovascular condition of humans associated with physical training, persistently performed sports and exercises. *Proc College Phys Educ Ass,* Columbus, Ohio, *60*:82-104, 1957.

127. MICHAEL, E. D., JR., and GALLON, A. J.: Pulse wave and blood pressure changes occurring during a physical training program. *Res Quart, 31*:43-59, March 1960.

128. PHILLIPS, E. E., JR.: Physical Fitness Changes in Adults Attributable to equal Periods of Training, Non-Training and Re-Training. Ph.D. Thesis, Physical Education, U. of Ill., 1960.

129. JOKL, E., and WELLS, J. B.: Exercise training and cardiac stroke force. In Raab, W. (Ed.): *Prevention of Ischemic Heart Disease.* Springfield, Thomas, 1966.

130. CURETON, T. K.: 300-500 calories exercise per day advised for adults. *Medical Tribune,* World-wide Report, May 17, 1965.
131. CURETON, T. K., with WHITE, W. H.: Exercises to keep fit. *Sports Illustrated,* August 1954.
132. CHAILEY-BERT, P., and FABRE-CHEVALIER: Contribution a l'etude des variations du cholesterol sanguin au cours des activités physiques. *Presse Med, 63:*21, March 19, 1955.
133. MONTOYE, VAN HUSS, *et al.*: The effects of exercise on blood cholesterol of middle-aged men. *Amer J Clin Nutr, 7:*139, 1959. Same study reported by Olson, H. W.: In *Phys Educator, 15:*135-137, Dec. 1958. Original project report to the National Institutes of Health, Grant No. H-2245, 1957.
134. POHNDORF, R. H.: Improvement in physical fitness of two middle-aged adults. Ph.D. Thesis, Physical Education, U. of Ill., 1957. In *Dissertation Abstracts, 17:*2493, 1957, and *Res Quart, 29:*180-192, May 1958.
135. MÉTIVIER, J. G.: The Effects of Five Different Physical Exercise Programs on the Blood Serum Cholesterol of Adult Women. Ph.D. Thesis, Physical Education, U. of Ill., 1960.
136. CAMPBELL, D. E.: A Study of the Influence of Several Physical Activities Upon the Blood Serum Cholesterol. EdD. Thesis, Colorado State College, 1961. (Financed by U.S. Public Health Grant).
137. GOLDING, L. A.: The Effects of Physical Training Upon the Total Serum Cholesterol. Ph.D. Thesis, Physical Education, U. of Ill., 1961. In *Res Quart, 32:*499-506, Dec. 1961.
138. GOLDING, L. A.: Serum cholesterol levels in adult men as effected by prolonged exercise. *Fed Proc, 21:*96, March-April 1962.
139. ROCHELLE, R. H.: Blood plasma cholesterol changes during a physical training program. *Res Quart, 32:*538-550, Dec. 1961.
140. JOHNSON, T. F., and WONG, H. Y. C.: Effects of exercise on plasma cholesterol and phospholipids in college swimmers. *Res Quart, 32:*514-521, Dec. 1961.
141. GOLDING, L. A.: The effects of physical training upon the total serum cholesterol. *Op. cit.*
142. MANN, G. V., *et al.* Importance of caloric disposition in cholesterol and lipo-protein metabolism of human subjects. *Fed Proc, 14:*442, March 1955, and in *New Eng J Med, 19:*25-28, 1955.
143. KRITCHEVSKY, D.: *Cholesterol.* New York, Wiley, 1958.
144. PAGE, I. H., *et al.*: Treatment of disorders of cholesterol mechanism. In Cook, R. P. (Ed.): *Cholesterol: Its Chemistry, Biochemistry and Pathology.* New York, Academic, 1958.
145. BORTZ, E. L.: Exercise, fitness and aging. In *Exercise and Fitness,* University of Illinois Colloquium. Chicago, Athletic Institute, 1960, pp. 1-9.
146. POWERS, B. S., and DiLUZIO, N. R.: Dietary cholesterol and adrenal regulation of plasma lipids. *Amer J Physiol, 195:*166-70, Oct. 1958.
147. HURXTHAL, L. M.: Blood cholesterol in thyroid disease. *Arch Intern Med* (Chicago), *51:*22-23, 1933.
148. CURETON, T. K.: Physical training helps to regulate and improve glandular functions. *Res Quart, 30:*266-84, Oct. 1959.
149. SKINNER, J. S.: The Effect of an Exercise Program on the Cholesterol and Triglycerides of the Blood Serum. Ph.D. Thesis, Physical Education. U. of Ill. 1963.

150. GARRETT, LEON; PANGLE, R. V., and MANN, G. V.: Effects of physical conditioning on coronary risk factors in men. *Fed Proc* (Abstract No. 733), *24*:262, March-April 1965.

151. KIREILIS, R. W., and CURETON, T. K.: The relationship of external fat to performance in physical education activities. *Res Quart, 18*:133-134, May 1947.

152. CURETON, T. K.: The value of hard endurance exercises and tests to produce changes in fat, metabolism and cardiovascular condition. *Vigor* (Johannesburg, South Africa), *2*:12-16, Sept. 1958; The long, slow, physical training build-up. *Canadian Aquatic News* (Erindale, Ontario), *1*:5+, Nov. 1958.

153. CURETON, T. K.: The effect of physical training, sports and exercises on weight, fat and tissue proportions. *Professional Contributions.* Washington, *Amer Acad Phys Educ,* Nov. 1958, pp. 25-40.

154. GOLDING, L. A.: The effects of physical training upon the blood serum cholesterol. *op. cit.*

155. GOLDING, *Ibid.*

156. GOLDING, L. A.: Serum cholesterol levels in adult men as affected by prolonged exercise, *op cit.*

157. UVNAS, B.: Sympathetic vasodilator outflow. *Physiol Rev, 34*:608-618, July, 1954.

158. ASMUSSEN, E.; NIELSEN, M., and WIETH-PEDERSEN, G.: Cortical or reflex control of respiration during muscular work. *Acta Physiol Scand, 6*:168, 1943.

159. MATEEF, D.: Respiration and achievement in physical work and sport. In Karvonen, M. J. (Ed.): *Sport Medicine.* Helsinki, Finnish Sport Med. Ass, pp. 158-160.

160. BEST, C. H., and TAYLOR, N. B.: Factors affecting the coronary circulation. In *The Physiological Basis of Medical Practice.* Baltimore, Williams & Wilkins, 1945, pp. 278-280.

161. GREGG, D. E., and SHIPLEY, R. E.: *Amer J Physiol, 141*:382, 1944.

162. BROWN, E. W., JR.; BUNNELL, I. L., and GREENE, DAVID G.: Effects of hemodynamic changes on the shape of the brachial arterial pressure curve. *Amer J Physiol, 179*:622, Dec. 1954.

163. ECKSTEIN, J. W., and ABBOUD, F. M.: Circulatory effects of sympathomimetic amines. *Amer Heart J, 63*:119-135, Jan. 1962.

164. SARNOFF, S. J., and MITCHELL, JERE H.: The regulation of the performance of the heart. *Amer J Med,* May 1961, pp. 747-771.

165. STARR, ISAAC, and WOOD, FRANCIS C.: Twenty-year studies with the ballistocardiograph. *Circulation, 23*:714-732, May 1961.

166. CHRISTENSEN, E. H.: Contributions to the physiology of severe muscular work. V. Minute volume and stroke volume of the heart during severe muscular work. *Arbeitsphysiol, 4*:470-502, 1931.

167. LINDGREN, P., and UVNAS, B.: Vasoconstrictor inhibition and vasodilator activation. Two functionally separate vasodilator mechanisms in the skeletal muscles. *Acta Physiol Scand, 33*:108-119, 1955.

168. SARNOFF, S. J.; BROCKMAN, S. K.; GILMORE, J. P.; LINDEN, R. J., and MITCHELL, J. H.: Regulation of ventricular contraction, the influence of cardiac sympathetic and vagal nerve stimulation on atrial and ventricular dynamics. *Circ Res, 8*:1108-1119, Sept. 1960.

169. OGAWA, Y.: *op. cit.,* pp. 765-769.

170. DAGGETT, W. M.; NUGENT, G. C.; CARR, P. W.; POWERS, P. C., and HARADA, Y.: In-

fluence of vagal stimulation on ventricular contractility, O_2 consumption and coronary flow. *Amer J Physiol, 212*:8-18, Jan. 1967.

171. CURETON and DU TOIT, *op. cit.*

172. CURETON, T. K.; CUNDIFF, D. E.; SLONIGER, E. L.; DU TOIT, S. F.: Further Studies of the Pre-ejection Intervals as Related to Physical Stress and Endurance Performances. Unpublished paper presented at Amer College of Sports Medicine Meetin Las Vegas, March 1967.

173. SLONIGER, *op. cit.*

174. CURETON, T. K. (with Eds.): The cardiovascular effects of exercise. *Roche Med Image, 8*:32-33, June 1966.

175. RODBARD, S.: Timing of the arterial sounds: an index of stroke output. Abstract No. 98, *Fed Proc, 25*:205, part I, March-April 1966.

176. RANDALL, W. C., and ROHSE, W. G.: The augmentor action of the sympathetic cardiac nerves. *Circ Res, 4*:470-475, July 1956.

177. CURETON and PHILLIPS, *op. cit.*

178. FARHI, ASHER: Physical Fitness of the U.S. Air Force Officers Defense Command. M.S. Thesis, Physical Education, U. of Ill., 1962.

179. CILLO, ANTHONY R.: An Evaluation of the Physical Activities and Fitness of Air Force Officers. M.S. Thesis, Physical Education, U. of Ill., 1963.

180. FARVAR, AGHDASS: The Effects of the Canadian X-BX on Physical Fitness of Women. M.S. Thesis, Physical Education, U. of Ill., 1964.

181. STALLMAN, R. K.: The Metabolic Cost of the 5BX Plan for Physical Fitness. M.S. Thesis, Physical Education, U. of Ill., 1964.

182. McMICHAEL, J., *et al.*: Postural changes in cardiac output and respiration in man. *Quar J Exp Physiol, 27*:55-71, 1931.

183. CHRISTENSEN, E. H.: Minutevolumen und Schlagvolumen des Herzens Wahrend Schwerer Korperlicher Arbeit. *Arbeitsphysiol, 4*:470-502, 1931.

184. CURETON, T. K., and POHNDORF, R. H.: Influence of wheat germ oil as a dietary supplement in a program of conditioning exercises with middle-aged subjects. *Res Quart, 26*:391-407, Dec. 1955.

185. BRANDFONBRENER *et al., op. cit.*

186. CURETON, T. K.: Comparison of methods for determining cardiac output. *Op. cit.*

187. SELYE, HANS: *Stress.* Montreal, Acta, Inc., 1950.

188. ZIMKIN and KOROBKOV, *op. cit.*

189. CURETON and POHNDORF, *op. cit.*

190. CURETON, T. K.: Improvements resulting from a U.S. Navy underwater swimming training program with and without dietary supplements. *Res Quart, 34*:440-453, Dec. 1963.

191. CURETON, T. K.: Summary of recent findings from dietary supplement studies in relationship to the possibility for improving athletic and cardiovascular performance. *Rep Int Congr Sport Sci*, Tokyo, 1964, pp. 214-220.

192. CURETON, T. K.: A physical fitness case study of Joie Ray, improving physical fitness from 60 to 70 years of age. *J Ass Phys Ment Rehab, 18*:64-72, 80, May-June 1964.

193. CURETON, T. K.: Results of progressive physical training for adult men swimming. *FIEP Bull, 1*:58-59, 1955.

194. HOLLOSZY, J. O.; SKINNER, J. S.; BARRY, A., and CURETON, T. K.: Effects of a six-month program of endurance exercises on physical work. *Amer J Cardiol, 14*:747-

762, Dec. 1964. *Ibid.*, on serum lipids, pp. 753-760. *Ibid.*, on cardiovascular functioning, pp. 761-770.

195. CURETON, T. K.: *Physical Fitness and Dynamic Health.* New York, Dial, 1965.

196. POHNDORF, R. H.: Improvement in Physical Fitness of Two Middle-Aged Adults. Ph.D. Thesis, Physical Education, U. of Ill., 1956.

197. RIBISL, *op. cit.* (ref. 101).

198. CURETON, T. K.: In *Exercise and Fitness.* Chicago, Athletic Institute, 1960, p. 155.

199. CURETON, T. K.: *Physical Fitness Appraisal and Guidance.* St. Louis, Mosby, 1947, p. 224.

200. HEUSNER, W. W.: Progressive Changes in the Physical Fitness of an Adult Male During a Season of Training for Competitive Swimming. Ph.D. Thesis, Physical Education, U. of Ill., 1955.

APPENDIX A

PROGRESSIVE PULSE RATIO TEST AS AN INDICATOR OF OXYGEN SHORTAGE (OR EXERCISE TOLERANCE) AND PREDICTOR OF OXYGEN AVAILABILITY FOR PROGRESSIVELY HARDER WORK INCREMENTS*

Explanation of Test

The *Progressive Pulse Ratio Test*, which has been in use in the University of Illinois Physical Fitness Research Laboratory since 1950[1] and which was introduced into the literature then, has been in constant use. In 1951, Cureton[2] made a parallel comparison of it with the brachial pulse waves and demonstrated that a low, straight-line plot corresponded to a tall, high velocity type of brachial pulse wave, and, conversely, that a sharp, rising ratio with a large angle to the base line and a "break" upward in the line paralleled the small, flat type of brachial pulse wave. Subsequent work by Michael[3] and by Michael and Cureton[4] related the brachial pulse wave to stroke volume, with correlations between amplitude of the primary systolic pulse wave and stroke volume as high as 0.91 and the amplitude related to computed velocity of the stroke as high as 0.83.[5] Factor analysis demonstrated that the ratio measured a different component of cardiovascular condition than the pulse rate recovery pulse counts. The ratio reflects the rise of the pulse rate over the sitting rate (i.e., the number of times it is greater). The pulse rate is counted beginning immediately after the work increment in each case, progressing in intensity from 12, to 18, to 24, to 30, to 36 steps per minute, and up to the tolerance point (angle of break) is related to O_2 intake capacity and blood flow. The ratio is poorly correlated with the Harvard Step Test but is more valid to reflect the oxygen used in the work or in recovery.[6] The pulse ratio plotted line parallels the O_2 debt line more closely than O_2 intake; but, as O_2 intake declines because of tension or fatigue or inadequate respiration, the "angle of break" occurs in the plotted line.

Research Methods Used in Validation Studies

Oxygen intake and oxygen debt determinations were made on each of the rates of stepping and were plotted against the ratio.[7] The ratio

---

*Prepared by Thomas K. Cureton, Jr.

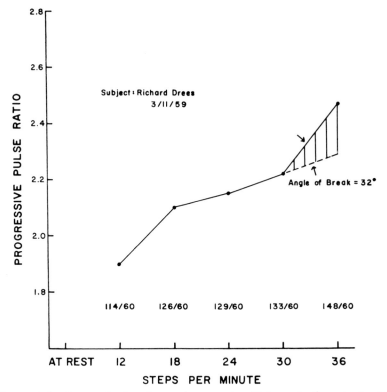

FIGURE A-1. Progressive bench stepping exercise. Pulse ratio (in pulse beats).

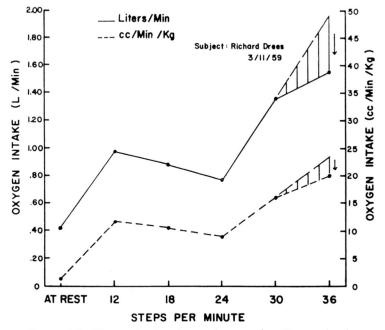

FIGURE A-2. Progressive bench stepping exercise. Oxygen intake.

improves as improvements are made in all out treadmill running time and in maximal oxygen intake capacity, and vice versa in deterioration from the peak of training. DeVries[8] obtained a correlation of 0.71 for the average ratio and the maximal oxygen intake, but the terminal angle of "break" indicates even a better relationship and shows where the oxygen deficiency begins. The initial angle shows parasympathetic or lethargic bias before the initial 1-minute step at 12 steps per minute, and the first point (12 steps per min) is usually discarded in determining the slope.

Improvement studies have been made to show that as less and less oxygen debt develops in the progressive stages of training, the terminal angle straightens out to make a straight line, or it may even turn downward in superior subjects due to greater oxygenization than normal in the experimental subject. The whole pulse ratio line is lowered for most subjects as progressive training is pursued. There are many improvement studies.[9-14]

Research Findings

The test reflects the established fact that the *increase* in pulse rate due to the work load must be measured without waiting a minute, as in the Harvard Step Test, if the data are to reflect the work done with any appreciable validity.[15, 16] Numerous authors have suggested the Harvard Step Test to reflect the work done, but there have been many objections to the low validity coefficients. This latter test reflects some part of the recovery pulse rates after the leg pumps have ceased pumping blood to the heart. The reasons for these low validity coefficients should be apparent when the factor analysis matrix is studied,[5] showing that the *rise in pulse rate* (sympatheticotonic) is not in the same factor column as the recovery pulse (parasympatheticotonic) response. Since these factors are reasonably independent, they are not duplicates.[5] This test is moderately valid to predict all-out capacity or maximal O_2 intake, but that is not its principal purpose. It aims rather to screen out people who develop oxygen deficiency after moderate exertion and to show the point at which a sudden oxygen insufficiency occurs (cf. Figs. A-1, A-2, A-3, A-4, A-5, A-6).

There is no objection to using the pulse rates from the 2-minute recovery pulse counts, but such pulse rates are dominated by vagus tone and do not represent the stroke output of the heart nor the sympatheticotonic increase during the work.

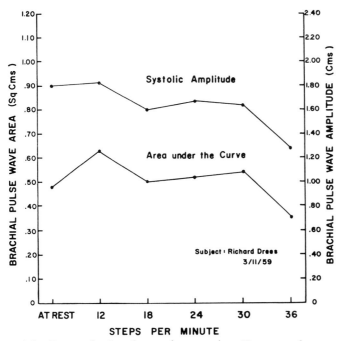

FIGURE A-3. Progressive bench stepping exercise. Heartograph measures.

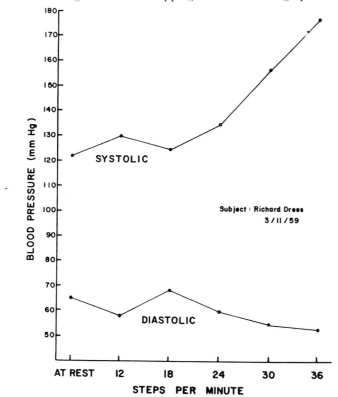

FIGURE A-4. Progressive bench stepping exercise. Blood pressures.

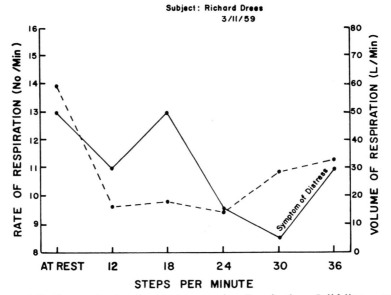

FIGURE A-5. Progressive bench stepping exercise. Respiration. Solid line = rate; broken line = number of respirations/min.

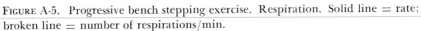

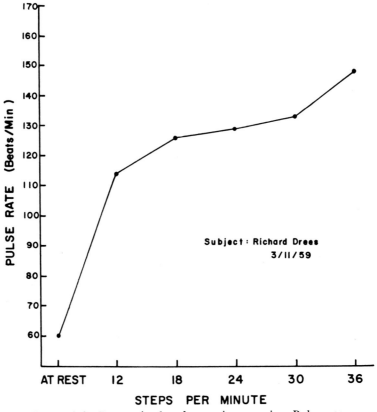

FIGURE A-6. Progressive bench stepping exercise. Pulse rate.

VALIDITY OF VARIOUS SUBMAXIMAL TESTS TO PREDICT PERFORMANCE

All-out Treadmill Run and All-out Step Test

	(Rank order rho's)
Astrand Predicted Maximal O$_2$ Intake vs All-out Step Test Time (N = 20)	0.65
Brachial pulse wave, systolic amplitude after Run-in-place (1 min) vs All-out Treadmill Run (7 mph, 8.6% grade) (N = 15 males)	0.65
Average Progressive Pulse Ratio Test vs All-out Step Test Time (N = 20)	0.59
Astrand Predicted Maximal O$_2$ Intake vs All-out Treadmill Run Time (N = 16 males)	0.59
Cureton's Progressive Pulse Ratio Terminal Angle of Break vs All-out Step Test Time (N = 20)	0.57
Cureton's Progressive Pulse Ratio Average Angle vs All-out Step Test Time (N = 20)	0.51
Cureton's Progressive Pulse Ratio Terminal Angle from Horizontal vs All-out Step Test Time (N = 20)	0.46
All-out Step Test Time (30 per min on 17-inch bench) vs All-out Treadmill Run Time (7 mph, 8.6% grade) (N = 16)	0.44
Cureton's Progressive Pulse Ratio (average of 5 ratios) vs All-out Treadmill Run Time (N = 16 males)	0.39
Sitting Brachial Pulse Wave, Systolic Amplitude vs All-out Treadmill Run Time (N = 17)	0.23
Sitting Brachial Pulse Wave, Systolic Amplitude (after 30-min warm-up) vs. All-out Treadmill Run Time (N = 17)	0.17
Cureton's Progressive Pulse Ratio Test, Angle of Break, vs All-out Treadmill Run Time (N = 18)	0.13
Cureton's Progressive Pulse Ratio, Terminal Angle from Horizontal vs All-out Treadmill Run Time (N = 16 males)	0.03

Effect of Warm-up on Progressive Pulse Ratio Test

Miss Yan-shu Liu tested seven subjects (6 males and 1 female) in three successive Progressive Pulse Ratio Tests (Cureton's Progression at 12, 18, 24, 30, and 36 steps per min) in the University of Illinois Physical Fitness Research Laboratory in 1961. The results are shown in Table A-1 showing that the average unwarmed-up trial (T$_1$) averaged 2.441, the second trial after a separation of 10 minutes averaged 2.394, and the third trial averaged 2.333 after the same rest interval. This corresponds to a 1.92 percent and 4.42 percent improvement, gains of 9 SS and 14 SS, respectively.

The Progressive Pulse Ratio, now in use over 15 years, is recommended as a substitute test for the treadmill run or the maximal oxygen intake test because:

1. It is relatively safer and can be stopped whenever there is a sharp break (oxygen deficiency) or when the computed ratio goes over 3.0. It is moderately correlated with O$_2$ intake capacity but is more highly correlated with O$_2$ debt.

2. It makes a graphical record to show how the subject adjusts to

TABLE A-I

RESULTS OF THREE SUCCESSIVE PROGRESSIVE (CURETON) PULSE RATIO TESTS
(Each series 10 min apart)

Subject	T_1	T_2	T_3
L-S Liu	2.53	2.32	2.32
F. L.	2.34	2.32	2.32
R. L.	2.35	2.39	2.37
J. S.	2.73	2.69	2.51
T. K. C.	2.20	2.17	2.13
E. L.*	2.57	2.57	2.34
G. Ma	2.37	2.30	2.34
	2.441	2.394	2.333

N = 7
Age range: 22 to 30 (except T.K.C., 59)

*Elizabeth Liu's project in Cureton's P.E. 452 course—the only female (*cf* Figs. A-7, A-8, A-9).

regularly increased intensities of work (Fig. A-10). The relationship is usually curvilinear of the graph itself.

3. The graph interests the subjects and reveals what is happening— satisfactory adjustment or lack of adjustment at progressive stages of work.

4. It eliminates all very expensive equipment, which is usually not available in most college or high school physical education departments.

5. The test has proved satisfactory, and some scoring tables are available for children, adolescents and adults.

6. Scales have been provided for the ratios as well as the recovery pulses.

References

1. CURETON, T. K.: In *Proceedings of the 55th Annual Convention.* Dallas, American Association for Health, Physical Education and Recreation, 1950, pp. 126-127.
2. CURETON, T. K.: *Physical Fitness of Champion Athletes.* Urbana, U. of Ill., 1951, p. 240.
3. MICHAEL, E. D.: Relationship Between the Heartometer and the Acetylene Method of Measuring Circulatory Fitness. M.S. Thesis, Physical Education, U. of Ill., 1949.
4. MICHAEL, E. D., and CURETON, T. K.: Effects of physical training on cardiac output at ground level and at 15,000 feet of simulated altitude. *Res Quart, 24*:446-452, Dec. 1953.

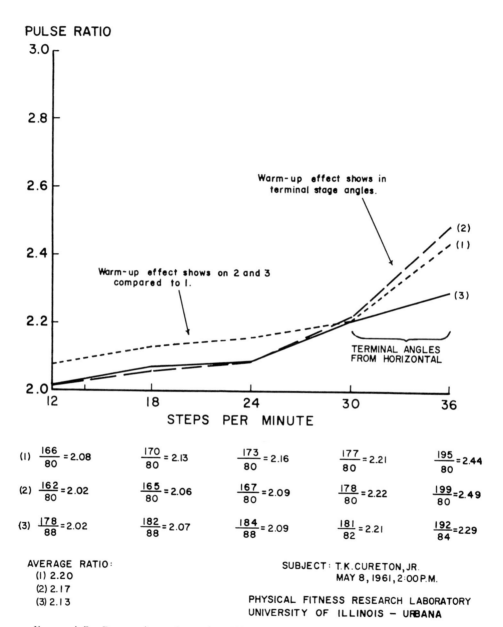

(1) $\dfrac{166}{80} = 2.08$ $\qquad$ $\dfrac{170}{80} = 2.13$ $\qquad$ $\dfrac{173}{80} = 2.16$ $\qquad$ $\dfrac{177}{80} = 2.21$ $\qquad$ $\dfrac{195}{80} = 2.44$

(2) $\dfrac{162}{80} = 2.02$ $\qquad$ $\dfrac{165}{80} = 2.06$ $\qquad$ $\dfrac{167}{80} = 2.09$ $\qquad$ $\dfrac{178}{80} = 2.22$ $\qquad$ $\dfrac{199}{80} = 2.49$

(3) $\dfrac{178}{88} = 2.02$ $\qquad$ $\dfrac{182}{88} = 2.07$ $\qquad$ $\dfrac{184}{88} = 2.09$ $\qquad$ $\dfrac{181}{82} = 2.21$ $\qquad$ $\dfrac{192}{84} = 229$

AVERAGE RATIO:
  (1) 2.20
  (2) 2.17
  (3) 2.13

SUBJECT: T.K.CURETON,JR.
MAY 8, 1961, 2:00P.M.

PHYSICAL FITNESS RESEARCH LABORATORY
UNIVERSITY OF ILLINOIS — URBANA

FIGURE A-7. Progressive pulse ratio. Effect of three successive tests (10 min apart).

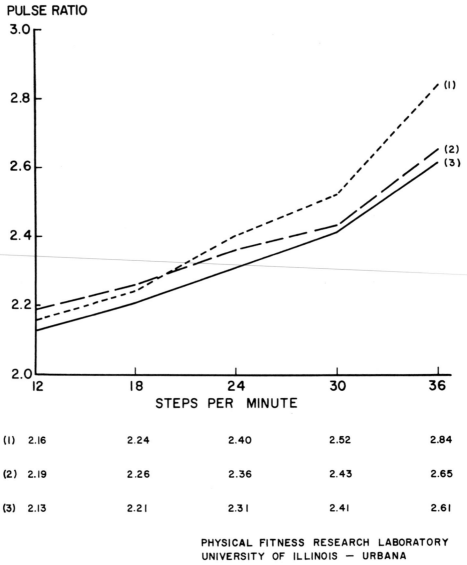

(1)	2.16	2.24	2.40	2.52	2.84
(2)	2.19	2.26	2.36	2.43	2.65
(3)	2.13	2.21	2.31	2.41	2.61

PHYSICAL FITNESS RESEARCH LABORATORY
UNIVERSITY OF ILLINOIS — URBANA
MAY, 1961

FIGURE A-8. Progressive pulse ratios at each rate of stepping. Mean for each of three successive tests (10 min apart). N = seven subjects.

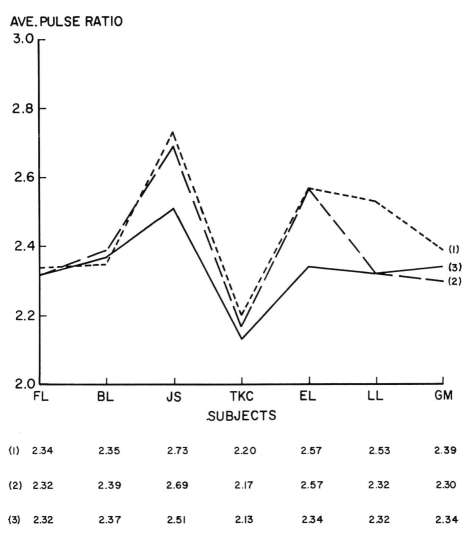

FIGURE A-9. Average progressive pulse ratio of each subject. Three successive tests (10 min apart).

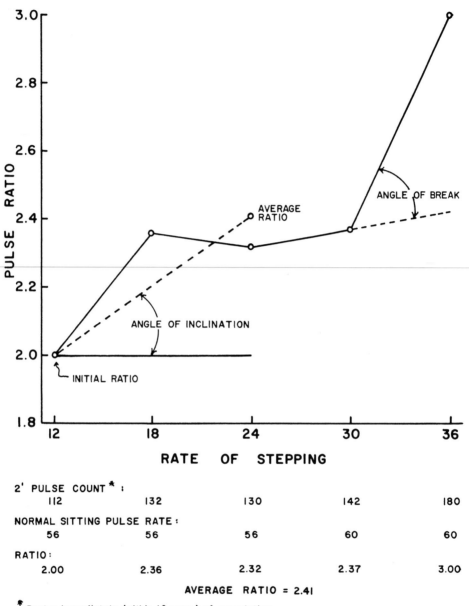

PULSE RATIO

RATE OF STEPPING

2' PULSE COUNT *:
  112   132   130   142   180

NORMAL SITTING PULSE RATE:
  56   56   56   60   60

RATIO:
  2.00   2.36   2.32   2.37   3.00

AVERAGE RATIO = 2.41

* Begins immediately (within 10 secs.) of completion.

FIGURE A-10. Progressive pulse ratio.

5. CURETON, T. K., and STERLING, L. F.: Factor analyses of cardiovascular test variables. *Sport Med, 2* (No. 4), Nov.-Dec. 1962.

6. CURETON, T. K.: Review of research to determine cardiovascular condition (1941-50). In *Proceedings of the 56th Annual Convention.* Detroit, American Association for Health, Physical Education and Recreation, 1951, pp. 167-177.

7. GRAY, MARY D.: The Progressive Pulse Ratio Test in Relation to Oxygen Intake and Oxygen Debt. M.S. Thesis, Physical Education, U. of Ill., 1952.

8. DeVRIES, HERBERT A.: The Progressive Pulse Ratio Test. In *Physiology of Exercise.* Dubuque, Brown, Wm. C., 1966.

9. CURETON, T. K.: The nature of cardiovascular condition (Part 3). *J Health, Phys Educ Rec, 12:*41-49, March-April 1958.

10. CURETON, *Ibid.* (Part 4), *12:*113-114, July-August 1958.

11. CURETON, T. K.: Improvements in cardiovascular condition of humans associated with physical training, persistently performed sports and exercises. *Proceedings of the 61st Annual Convention.* College Physical Education Association, 1958.

12. VINCITORE, MICHAEL A.: The Effects of a Physical Conditioning Program on the Progressive Pulse Ratio Test of Adult Men. M.S. Thesis, Physical Education, U. of Ill., 1951.

13. KRISTUFEK, CHARLES J.: Effect of Endurance Training on an Adult Subject. M.S. Thesis, Physical Education, U. of Ill., 1951.

14. CURETON, T. K.: Physical fitness improvements of a middle-aged man, with brief reviews of related studies. *Res Quart, 23:*149-160, May 1952.

15. CURETON, T. K.: Experimental and statistical analyses of the step test. In *Endurance of Young Men.* Washington, National Society for Research in Child Development, vol. X, No. 40, 1945, pp. 187-194.

16. MONTOYE, HENRY J.: Interrelations of maximal pulse rate during moderate exercise, recovery pulse rate and post-exercise. *Res Quart, 11:*3-11, Oct. 1940.

CURETON'S SPECIFICATIONS FOR PROGRESSIVE PULSE RATIO TEST (STEPS OR SQUATS)*

1. (a) Seat subject 5 minutes. Count sitting pulse for 30 seconds. (b) After 30 seconds count sitting pulse for 30 seconds again. (c) If pulse is stable (+ beat), go on with the test. If not, count sitting pulse again and continue until two successive counts are the same. If there is still fluctuation, use the average.

2. Have the subject stand up. Count out the timing of the stepping at 5 seconds for each complete trip (12 per min), 2½ seconds *up* and 2½ seconds *down*. Demonstrate. Ask the subject to count the number of trips he makes in 1 minute at 12 per minute. Start the subject on the even minute at the start of one revolution of the minute hand on a stopwatch or Eastman photo-timer. Count for the subject so

---

*Steps up and down on a stool or bench (15 to 17 inches high). An alternate test may be done with full knee-bend squats, standing with one foot a few inches ahead of the other, fingertips touching the floor on each dip. The present tables, however, apply strictly to the stepping procedure.

that one complete trip coincides with 5 seconds on the clock. Continue stepping for exactly 1 minute. Tell the subject to sit down. Then after 10 seconds, count pulse for 2 minutes (i.e. begin the pulse count exactly 10 seconds after the even minute).

3. Compute the pulse ratio and plot the second point while the subject remains seated. Recheck the sitting rate at least twice. Continue until the pulse is stable, and record in terms of b/min as denominator.

4. Count the rate of stepping at 3.33 seconds for one complete trip, 18 per minute. Three trips in 10 seconds. Demonstrate. Ask the subject to count the number of steps or use a pulse counter. Step the subject at this rate for exactly one minute. At the end, seat the subject and after 10 seconds count the pulse for 2 minutes. Compute the pulse ratio and plot the point.

5. After 2 to 3 minutes, check pulse at least twice for 15 seconds. Continue until the pulse rate is stable. Record the sitting rate as denominator.

6. Explain the rate of stepping at 24 steps per minute, $2\frac{1}{2}$ seconds per trip. Demonstrate. Ask the subject to count his trips. Step the subject for exactly 1 minute. Have the subject sit, and after 10 seconds count the pulse for 2 minutes.

7. Repeat step 5.

8. Explain to the subject the rate of stepping at 30 per minute. Demonstrate, one second *up* and one second *down*. Ask the subject to count the steps. Stop the subject for exactly 2 minutes. Have the subject sit, and after 10 seconds count the pulse for 2 minutes. Compute the pulse ratio and plot the fourth point.

9. Recheck the sitting pulse rate at least twice and continue until the pulse is stable. Record the sitting rate as the denominator.

10. Explain the rate of stepping at 36 per minute. Demonstrate or count out three trips *up* and *down* in 5 seconds. Ask the subject to count the number of steps, and step the subject for exactly 1 minute.

Additional Notations for Progressive Pulse Ratio Test

1. The subject should not hold his breath during the exercise nor during the recovery period; he should breathe normally throughout the test.

2. Unreliability is usually in the lack of stability in the initial sitting pulse rate and, to some extent, in each succeeding sititng pulse rate. It is a necessary precaution to count the sitting pulse at least three times for 30 seconds each time and to use the lowest pulse rate obtained. In very careful work, each subject should be tested two or three times on succeeding days for reliability comparisons.

3. All data should show on the graph, including the computed pulse ratios and 30-second pulse counts as given successively during the

recuperation phase (at least 3 counts for 30 sec each); also, both the numerator and denominator should show to permit rechecking all of the arithmetic of the computed pulse ratio.

4. In posting and plotting the graphs, it is important to standardize the pattern of the graphs. Use No. 358-11 K and E thin graph sheets (8½ by 11 inches), having twenty squares to the inch and red lines, so that one graph can be matched over another by superimposition and being held up to the light. The base line should be four large squares from the bottom of each sheet, labeled *Rate of stepping (or squatting)* with five small squares for each stepping (or squatting)

TABLE A-II

PROGRESSIVE PULSE RATIO STANDARD SCORE TABLE
FOR YOUNG MEN (15 to 25 Yrs)

Initial Pulse Ratio	Average Pulse Ratio	Angle of Inclination	Angle of Break	Angle Between 30 and 36 Step Ratio	Standard Score
1.725	1.954	2.27°	−19.61°	− 3.50°	100
1.763	1.995	5.52°	−14.35°	1.78°	95
1.800	2.040	8.76°	− 9.08° ·	7.06°	90
1.838	2.085	12.01°	− 3.82°	12.34°	85
1.875	2.130	15.26°	1.45°	17.62°	80
1.913	2.175	18.51°	6.72°	22.90°	75
1.950	2.220	21.75°	11.98°	28.18°	70
1.988	2.265	25.00°	17.25°	33.46°	65
2.025	2.310	28.25°	22.51°	38.74°	60
2.063	2.351	31.49°	27.28°	44.02°	55
2.100	2.400	34.74°	33.04°	49.30°	50
2.138	2.445	37.99°	38.31°	54.58°	45
2.175	2.490	41.23°	43.57°	59.86°	40
2.213	2.535	44.48°	48.84°	65.14°	35
2.250	2.580	47.73°	54.18°	70.42°	30
2.288	2.625	50.98°	59.45°	75.70°	25
2.325	2.670	54.22°	64.71°	80.98°	20
2.363	2.715	54.47°	69.98°	86.26°	15
2.400	2.760	60.72°	75.24°	91.54°	10
2.437	2.805	63.96°	80.51°	96.92°	5
2.475	2.850	67.21°	85.77°	102.20°	0
N = 53	N = 53	N = 53	N = 53	N = 50	
Mean = 2.100	Mean = 2.40	Mean = 34.74°	Mean = 33.04°	Mean = 49.30°	
σ = .125	σ = .045	σ = 10.824	σ = .1755	σ = 17.60	

TABLE A-III

PROGRESSIVE PULSE RATIO TEST (CURETON)

(Men 26 to 60 yrs)

Classification	Ratio (12 Steps Per Min)	Ratio (18 Steps Per Min)	Ratio (24 Steps Per Min)	Ratio (30 Steps Per Min)	Ratio (36 Steps Per Min)	Avg Ratio of 5 Ratios	Angle Between 24 and 30 Steps per Min	Angle Between 30 and 36 Steps per Min	Avg Angle*	Standard Score	Percentile
Excellent	1.72	1.73	1.72	1.79	1.62	1.86	0	0	1	100	99.9
	1.76	1.78	1.80	1.88	1.76	1.93	0	0	5	95	99.7
	1.80	1.84	1.88	1.98	1.90	1.99	0	0	8	90	99.2
Very good	1.85	1.90	1.95	2.07	2.03	2.06	3	4	12	85	98.2
	1.89	1.96	2.03	2.16	2.17	2.13	8	9	16	80	96.7
	1.93	2.02	2.10	2.26	2.31	2.20	13	15	19	75	93.3
Above average	1.98	2.07	2.18	2.35	2.45	2.26	18	20	23	70	88.4
	2.02	2.13	2.26	2.45	2.59	2.33	24	26	26	65	81.6
	2.07	2.19	2.34	2.54	2.73	2.40	29	31	30	60	72.6
Average	2.11	2.24	2.42	2.63	2.87	2.46	34	36	33	55	61.8
	2.15	2.30	2.49	2.73	3.01	2.53	39	42	37	50	50.0
	2.20	2.36	2.57	2.82	3.15	2.60	44	47	40	45	38.2
Below average	2.24	2.42	2.65	2.92	3.28	2.66	49	53	44	40	27.4
	2.28	2.48	2.72	3.01	3.42	2.73	54	58	48	35	18.4
	2.33	2.53	2.80	3.10	3.56	2.80	59	64	51	30	11.5

Poor	2.37	2.59	2.88	3.19	3.70	2.86	64	69	55	25	6.7
	2.42	2.65	2.96	3.29	3.84	2.93	70	74	58	20	3.6
	2.46	2.70	3.03	3.39	3.98	3.00	75	80	62	15	1.8
Very poor	2.50	2.76	3.11	3.48	4.12	3.06	80	85	65	10	.82
	2.55	2.82	3.19	3.57	4.26	3.13	85	91	69	5	.35
	2.59	2.88	3.26	3.67	4.40	3.20	90	96	72	0	.14
Mean	2.154	2.303	2.493	2.728	3.007	2.530	38.9	41.96	36.9		
Sigma	.145	.186	.258	.314	.463	.223	17.08	18.10	11.9		
Number	116	116	113	113	96	85	90	74	64		
Range	1.60-2.44	1.90-2.84	1.90-3.29	1.90-2.88	2.10-4.70	2.06-3.28	0-80	0-79	12-76		

*Average angle found as follows: Plot average ratio of 24 steps per minute. Draw line from ratio of 2.0 through average ratio. Measure angle of line. Draw line from this ratio horizontally; then connect the plotted ratios as plotted at 18 and 24 steps/min. Measure the angle.

TABLE A-IV
RATING SCALE FOR PROGRESSIVE PULSE RATES
(Men 26 to 60 Yrs)

Classification	Total 2' Pulse Count After 12 Steps per Min	Total 2' Pulse Count After 18 Steps per Min	Total 2' Pulse Count After 24 Steps per Min	Total 2' Pulse Count After 30 Steps per Min	Total 2' Pulse Count After 36 Steps per Min	Standard Score	Percentile
Excellent	71	77	84	98	105	100	99.9
	80	86	94	109	118	95	99.7
	89	95	104	119	130	90	99.2
Very good	97	105	114	130	143	85	98.2
	106	114	124	141	156	80	96.7
	115	123	134	152	168	75	93.3
Above average	123	132	144	162	181	70	88.4
	132	142	154	173	193	65	81.6
	141	151	164	184	206	60	72.6
Average	149	160	175	195	218	55	61.8
	158	169	185	206	231	50	50.0
	167	178	195	217	244	45	38.2
Below average	175	188	205	227	256	40	27.4
	184	197	215	238	269	35	18.4
	193	206	225	249	281	30	11.5

Poor	201	216	235	260	294	25	6.7
	210	225	245	271	306	20	3.6
	219	234	255	281	319	15	1.8
Very poor	227	243	265	292	332	10	.82
	236	252	276	303	344	5	.35
	245	262	286	314	357	0	.14
Mean	157.9	169.3	184.6	205.8	231.0		
Sigma	28.9	30.8	33.6	36.03	41.9		
Number	115	114	113	112	96		
Range	100—226	100—238	120—306	120—309	120—370		

count. The vertical axis is labeled *pulse ratio* and is plotted one full
large square in from the left hand margin with five small squares for
each ten of pulse ratio.

5. In scoring the progressive pulse ratio, the following methods may be
    used: (a) Average all pulse ratios at 12, 18, 24, and 30, and 36 steps
    per minute. (b) Measure the angle to the horizontal using the best
    line through all the points unless there is a sharp break upward at
    one point; in this case, the point should be noted as well as the initial
    angle and the post-break average angle.

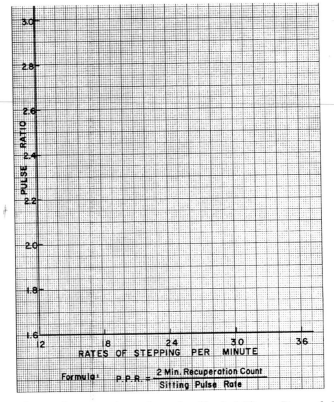

FIGURE A-11. Cureton's progressive pulse ratio. Physical Fitness Research Laboratory,
U. of Ill.

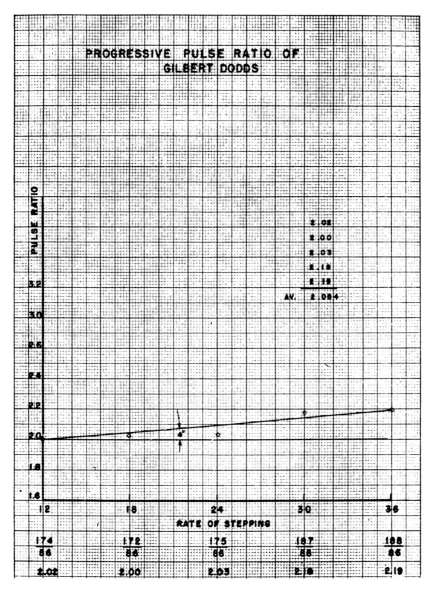

FIGURE A-12. Very superior subject, a highly trained champion miler. Physical Fitness Research Laboratory, U. of Ill.

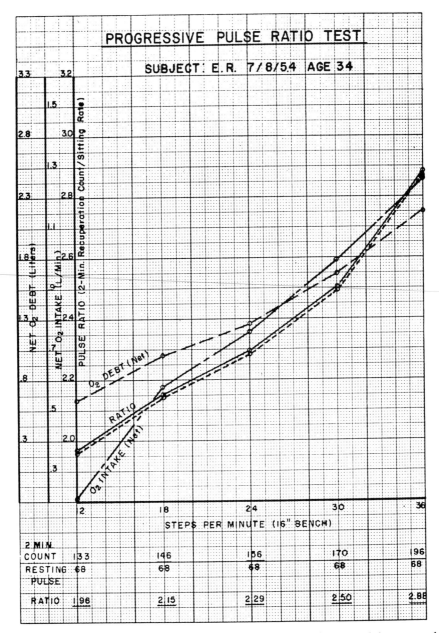

FIGURE A-13. Fairly good male subject. Slopes upward without sharp break in oxygen debt, oxygen intake, or ratio plots.

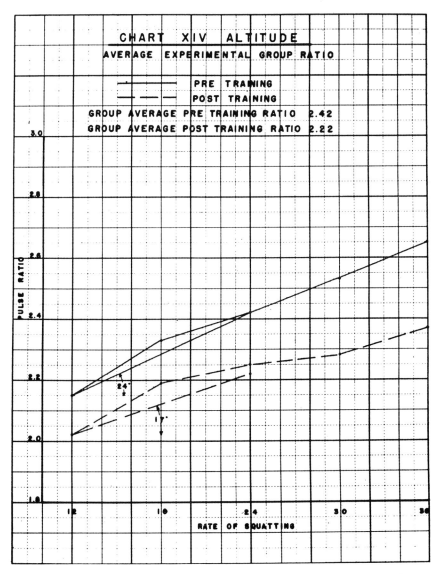

FIGURE A-14. Improvement in 24 weeks of training, comparing pre-training with post-training data by the progressive pulse ratio test.

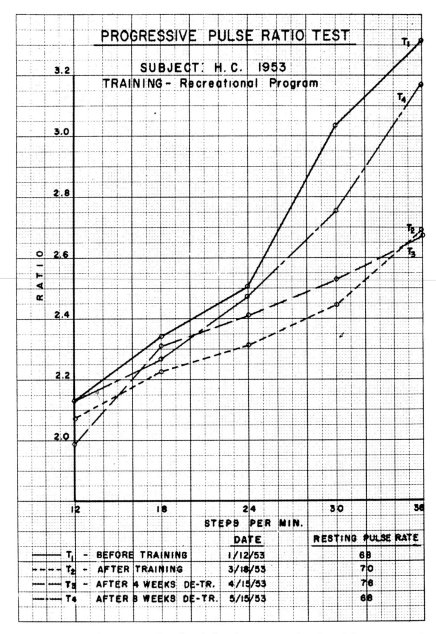

FIGURE A-15.   Record of 4 months of training in a recreational activity program by the progressive pulse ratio test.

Examples of Oxygen Intake and Debt with Bend in the PP Ratio Line

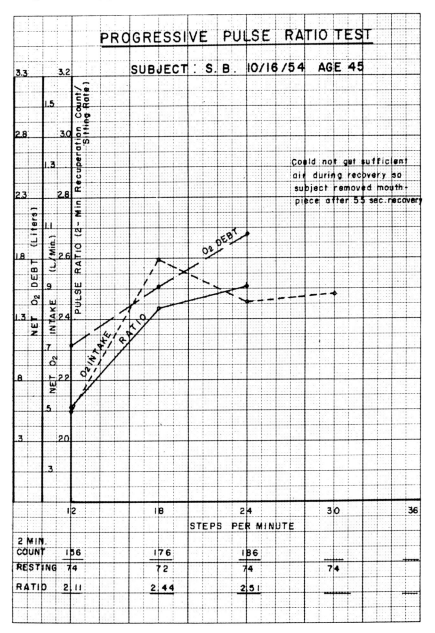

FIGURE A-16.

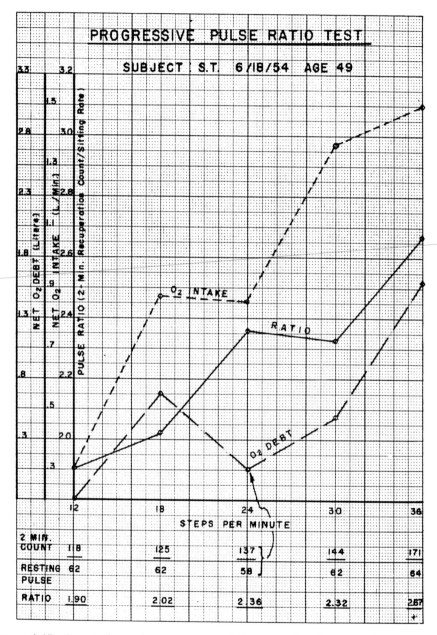

FIGURE A-17. Progressive ratio plot tends to follow the plot of oxygen debt; or oxygen intake declines, and the oxygen debt goes up as does the ratio plot.

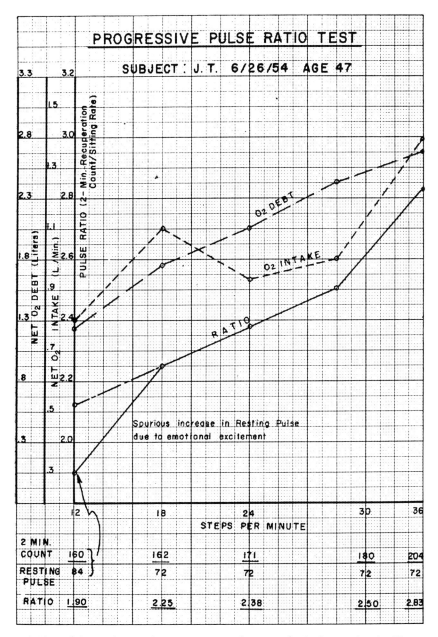

FIGURE A-18. High spurious pulse rate at start of test results in low ratio. At 36 steps per minute, a favorable warm-up with upturn of oxygen intake results in slight drop in slope of the oxygen debt plot.

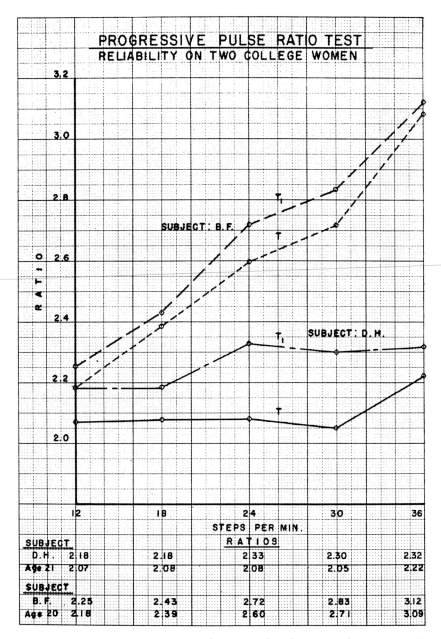

FIGURE A-19. Reliability by retest, two subjects repeating the progressive ratio test (1 week apart, no training between).

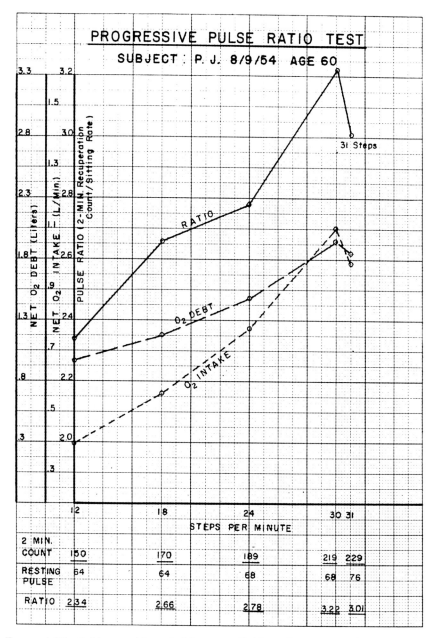

FIGURE A-20. Subject could not hold pace or finish at the 36-step-per-minute rate of stepping.

APPENDIX B

VALIDITY OF TESTING CARDIOVASCULAR FITNESS BY THE SPHYGMOGRAPH (EXTERNAL CUFF, HEARTOGRAPH) METHOD WITH THE CAMERON AND RELATED METHODS*

The Heartograph

The Cameron heartometer makes a circular graph, each revolution of which requires 1 minute, utilizing 60 cycle current, 110 v. to operate the machine. The brachial pulse wave is picked up by a pneumatic cuff set with the lower edge even with the bend of the elbow with the palm upward to prevent any twist in the artery. Cureton[1] has stated operational instructions, quite in addition to those furnished by the Cameron Company,[2] after 20 years of experimentation with the machine. The subject should be seated quietly to start and should be admonished to relax, especially the arm on which the cuff is placed. Preferably 5 minutes should be required in the quiet sitting position before taking the test; then after standing 1 minute quietly on both feet, the standing record is taken; finally, after a brisk run-in-place at 180 steps per minute with feet lifted 4 inches from the floor, the postexercise graph is taken. Each time, the blood pressures are taken with the right side pen before the pulse wave is graphed so that the pressure level of the cuff may be set at approximately 10 mm Hg above the diastolic pressure level. This is to obtain the optimal wave since the amplitude will be depressed if the wave is taken below the diastolic level or much above that level (Figs. B-1, B-2, B3).

About 1945, the instrument came into use in our laboratory, and considerable work was done to establish its characteristics and the best method of using it for studying cardiovascular condition of normal subjects. Several of the earliest studies to determine its validity and reliability were reported by Cureton.

Progress in Understanding the Wave, Logical Analysis

The heartograph reflects the heart output, beat to beat, slightly modified from the internal pressure pulse by its volume characteristics, the skin and fat, neuromuscular tension in the arm, as the pressure pulse is picked up by the pneumatic cuff and is transmitted to a bellows which,

---

*Prepared by Thomas K. Cureton, Jr.

118

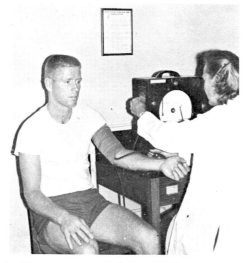

FIGURE B-1. Heartometer test given to subject in sitting position.

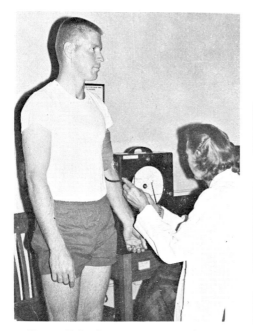

FIGURE B-2. Heartometer test given to subject in standing position.

FIGURE B-3. Heartometer test given to subject in running position. (Pulse wave is taken standing.)

FIGURE B-4.   The Cameron heartometer. Shown with part of the case cut away to reveal the bellows. In upper left, on rear of the case, a strain gauge has been affixed to the bellows to permit electrical pick-up of the motion of the bellows.

almost frictionless, in turn operates a set of lights and a vertically suspended lever. The heartograph records the forces of the heart's initial impulses and superimposes the volume characteristics due to expansion of the vessel itself. Its circulatory interpretation is cardio (heart force) and vascular (vessel), involving both. Except for slight losses, its vertical amplitude is directly derived from the "explosive" contraction of the heart's *initial impulse,* this slightly dampened by the effect of peripheral resistance in the aortic tree and losses in transmission through the arm tissues. Nevertheless, it reveals important characteristics about the circulation, is somewhat more reliable than auscultation procedures, and various studies of its reliability and validity indicate that it is extremely useful.

The heartometer is primarily a circulatory device, recording blood pressure by a switch which operates at 0.01 mm of movement of the mercury column in a calibrating device. It is to be distinguished from the electrocardiogram, which is electrical and depends upon current flow through tissues of changeable resistance in the heart and body; the heartometer is mechanical, although the clock which rotates the dial is electrical, and may be thought of like the ballistocardiogram, which is made by forces from the heart itself being used to move the body in an action-and-reaction relationship. The forces likewise move the blood, and the amount of force affects the amount of blood moved. In the BCG the preferred physical equation is $F = Ma$, assuming no friction; with the heartograph, the preferred equation is $Ft = Mv$. The contractile force of the heart (F) acts for a given time (t) to equal the momentum of the blood moved (Mv). In a given cycle for a given subject, the F is proportional to v, so the amplitude is interpreted primarily as a *velocity* wave, as Starr has described it.

Nervous and Hormonal Regulation of Heart Output

The heart cannot put out blood that it cannot get from the veins. The movements of the muscles, the involuntary twitches, and sometimes posture all aid in returning the blood. Good muscular tone helps like an elastic stocking to support the veins. Millions of people have poor venous return, so millions have poor circulation. The key to strengthening the circulation, and also the central or brachial pulse wave, is the muscular pumping, aided by nervous and hormonal stimulation and regulation of the vessels and the heart. Uvnas[3] has pointed out that the sympathetic vasodilator outflow aids the circulation in the muscles and probably in the heart and lungs. These stimuli probably dilate the minute sphincter (sluice gate) valves at the ends of the arterioles, which have been shown in recent electronic microscopic research to be regulated by nerve fibrils.[4] At these arteriolar-venule junctions, the blood flow may be affected by nervous tension (to restrict) and by temperature and temporary rise of peripheral systolic blood pressure (to open), thus letting blood into the capillary beds and relieving the central vascular bed of excess blood. There may also be hormonal regulation of these junctions. It is thought that the fall in total peripheral resistance, which occurs shortly after beginning an exercise, is due mainly to the opening of many of these "sluice gates." This would result in more blood flow and a larger pulse wave. If the blood pressure builds up and the sphincter valves do not open, then very high peripheral resistance would result—and this is the danger in sudden, hard exercises for untrained people. When the pulse wave responds almost immediately after a run-in-place, the response is typical of a "trained" individual, and "untrained" individuals are known to respond more slowly. Cureton[5] demonstrated that the highly trained endurance athletes from several parts of the world had very tall, sharp brachial waves, probably due to sympathetic stimulation of the veins returning the blood to the heart (ref. 5, p. 187).

The Inotropic Dimension Reflects Sympatho-adrenergic Stimulation

Sympathetic stimuli, resulting in secretion of norepinephrine directly into the heart tissue, also cause greater contractions of the heart fibers.[6] In fact, these secretions through the sympathetic nerves greatly augment the heart stroke *vigor* and account for a considerable part of the vertical (inotropic) dimensions of the brachial pulse waves.[7] Such stimulation may be cerebral or due to exercise. Adrenaline and norepinephrine also are secreted into the blood by the adrenal medulla, and such hormones act to reinforce the heart action, as do the accelerator nerves of the heart from the sympathetic chain. This sympathetic state results in better circulation and more work capacity. Athletes in a high state of training are usually "more ready" and have ready command of such reserves to activate the circulation; whereas older people, out of training, respond slowly and sluggishly. Physical training helps to develop these reserves.[8] The vagi nerves tend to slow the heart rate but doubtfully play any part in increasing the vigor of the heart stroke, as they are described as ending in the auricles.[9] In sympatheticotonia, the pre-ejection intervals usually shorten, especially the ICP (isovolumic period) which appears to be more sensitive than the EML (electro-mechanical lag); if the sympathetic stimulus is enough, both can shorten as in TP (tension period, the sum of both).[10] The vagi probably act to permit a more complete diastolic filling and greater coronary circulation; whereas, the sympathetic nerves augment the diastolic end-pressure before ejection.

Cureton demonstrated that mental "challenge" of a competitive nature

FIGURE B-5. In a single individual, serial changes in brachial pulse wave from normal to sympatheticotonic type following a challenge, race, and recovery. Graphs show serial changes in brachial pulse wave: *1.* Normal quiet sitting. *2.* After being challenged to a 4-mile steeplechase run. *3.* Immediately after 4-mile run in 32 minutes (winner). *4.* Five minutes after run. *5.* Fifteen minutes after run. *6.* Thirty-eight minutes after run. *7.* Fifty-two minutes after run. While sitting at a desk and having just taken a sitting brachial pulse wave in the quiet resting state, subject was interrupted from his work by three young men who challenged him to a 4-mile cross-country run. Quiet resting wave is shown as: *1.* When there was no thought of running. *2.* Changes induced first by mental excitement. *3.* Just after the run. *4, 5, 6, 7.* During recovery. In sympatheticotonia, the velocity of the brachial pulse wave increases with amplitude, the time of blood ejection from the heart gets shorter, and pulse pressure increases. After 52 minutes of recovery, pulse rate and amplitude are back to normal, but diastolic pressure is still low, probably indicating that the small blood vessels retain some dilatation. Peripheral resistance is still lower than normal, and systolic pressure is low.

SERIAL CHANGES IN THE BRACHIAL PULSE WAVE FROM NORMAL TO SYMPATHETICOTONIC TYPE, IN A SINGLE
INDIVIDUAL, FOLLOWING A CHALLENGE, A REST AND RECOVERY

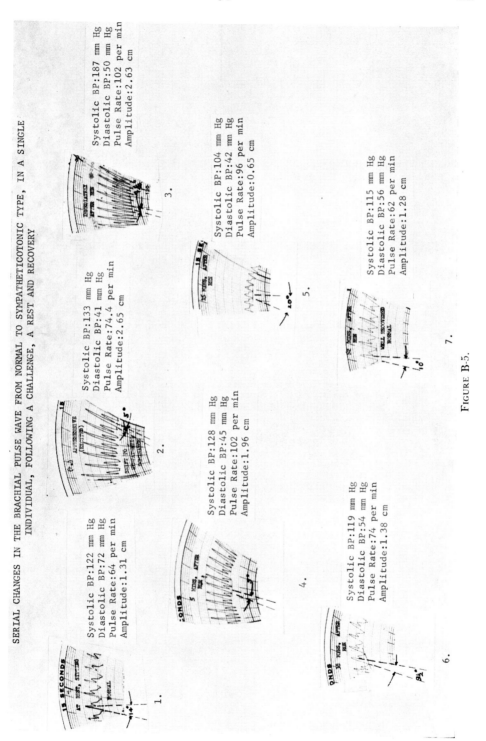

Systolic BP:122 mm Hg
Diastolic BP:72 mm Hg
Pulse Rate:64 per min
Amplitude:1.31 cm

Systolic BP:133 mm Hg
Diastolic BP:41 mm Hg
Pulse Rate:74.4 per min
Amplitude:2.65 cm

Systolic BP:187 mm Hg
Diastolic BP:50 mm Hg
Pulse Rate:102 per min
Amplitude:2.63 cm

Systolic BP:128 mm Hg
Diastolic BP:45 mm Hg
Pulse Rate:102 per min
Amplitude:1.96 cm

Systolic BP:104 mm Hg
Diastolic BP:42 mm Hg
Pulse Rate:96 per min
Amplitude:0.65 cm

Systolic BP:119 mm Hg
Diastolic BP:54 mm Hg
Pulse Rate:74 per min
Amplitude:1.38 cm

Systolic BP:115 mm Hg
Diastolic BP:56 mm Hg
Pulse Rate:62 per min
Amplitude:1.28 cm

FIGURE B-5.

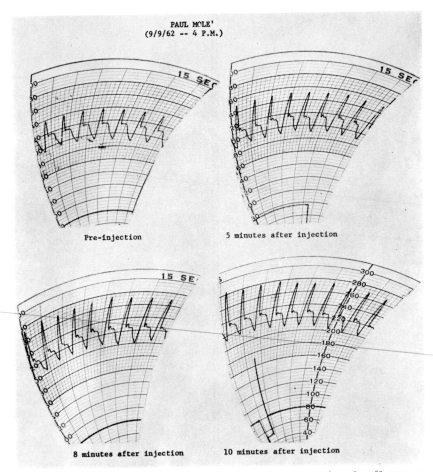

FIGURE B-6. Results of injecting adrenaline into a human to show its effect upon the heartograph.

(sympathetic stimulation) resulted in a sudden increase in the brachial pulse wave that was almost as great as the actual sympathetic excitement of the physical exertion itself. Such stimulation apparently affects the adrenal glands, and also works on the heart muscle by norepinepherine secreting into the heart muscle fibers through sympathetic nerves. The combined effect is known as the sympatho-adrenergic effect (Fig. B-5).

Dr. John Holloszy, as a member of the University of Illinois research team in the Physical Fitness Research Laboratory, injected adrenaline into the cubital vein of several subjects to observe the effect upon the brachial pulse wave. All subjects responded the same way: the amplitude was greatly increased (Fig. B-6).

The trained endurance athletes seem to have much greater nervous and hormonal reserves and are capable of greater endurance terminal efforts. At the end of all-out treadmill, or ergometer bicycle, or actual run tests, the blood samples show greater eosinopenia, associated with shorter ICP and TP intervals, and lower pH of the venous blood.[11, 12, 13]

Sophisticated Mathematical Analyses of Pressure Pulse Waves

In addition, the advanced scholar, should note the many attempts to analyze the pressure pulse waves by sophisticated mathematical techniques.[14, 15, 16] No attempt will be made to repeat what is in these analyses. A few of the more important references were given. For a more complete analysis, reference should be made to works by R. Rushmer,[17] Wiggers,[18] E. O. Attinger,[19] and D. A. McDonald.[20] This section will be confined to practical physiological and biometrical experiments in which we have been engaged.

The very early work on the volume curves began with the report of Yandell Henderson (1906),[21] but Otto Frank[22] studied the shape of the human pulse wave as early as 1899. He was more concerned with pulse wave transmission time than fitness of the heart. Wiggers'[23] work was the classical work from 1928 to 1952 summarized in his two books.[24, 25] Hamilton[26] came into this period after 1940 and published studies on the patterns of the arterial pressure waves. His work was with dogs, and data on aortas were obtained from stretch and rebound experiments after the dogs were dead.

In more recent years the laboratory studies have involved humans, as typified by the study by Brown, Bunnell and Greene,[27] who recorded arterial pressure pulse waves "showing the typical initial peak, followed by the dicrotic notch, and then a second peak on the anacrotic limb of the dicrotic wave." They demonstrated that the Valsalva effect to increase the thoracic pressure produced elevated waves, especially the dicrotic wave. It was concluded that the stroke volume and the total peripheral resistance of the aortic tree affected the waves. Skouby[28] concluded that the pull of the heart on the aorta during the isometric period of contraction initiated "extra oscillations" before the peak of the primary peak.

Flattened Pulse Waves Indicate Shortage of Myocardial Oxygen

The medically preferred method of detecting shortage of oxygen (and circulation) to the myocardium has been to use the double Master's test. It has been long studied and has considerable support by Master's many articles, by Gubner, Bruce and others, Such a shortage presents the difficulty of occurring in the healthiest athletes and others considered quite normal.

Another method preferred by us is the one we have used for several years,[29] namely, to observe the "decrement" or drop in amplitude of the

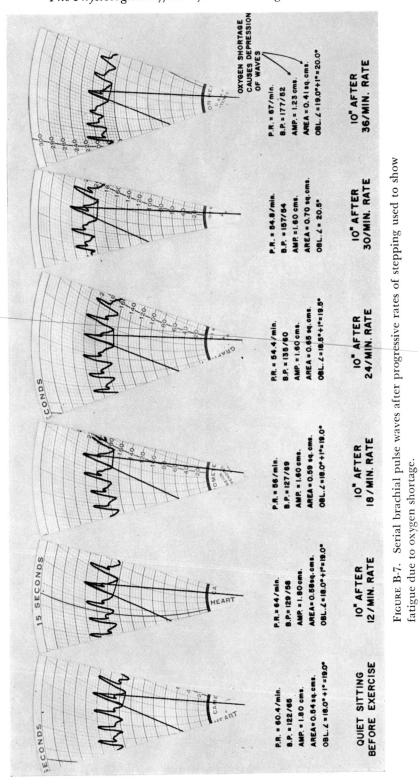

FIGURE B-7.   Serial brachial pulse waves after progressive rates of stepping used to show fatigue due to oxygen shortage.

brachial pulse wave in the progressive pulse ratio series of "step tests" (at 12, 18, 24, 30 and 36 steps per minute, refer to Appendix A); or before and after the Harvard Step Test; or before and after a treadmill run: (1) 4-minute jog, 7 mph, 8.6% grade, (2) in an all-out treadmill run (7 to 10 mph, 8.6% grade). In the quiet state, the angle on the front face of the wave is important and is highly related to "obliquity angle."

Figure B-7 shows the decrement after the progressive pulse ratio series. It shows in the last 36-step rate. This decrement test can be applied after 1 minute of running, and any person developing a pronounced decrement should be examined.

Cureton and Massey[30] reported that similated altitude in a decompression chamber produced a depression of amplitude proportional to the lowering of barometric pressure and lowering the availability of the available oxygen to the subjects, who recovered the lost amplitude after the oxygen was restored to them (Fig. B-8). There was a parallel depression in the T-waves of the highest precordial waves from the electrocardiogram.[31] They also reported that the amplitude or area was the best of several quiet-state cardiovascular tests to predict endurance.

Internally and Externally Taken Waves Are Similar on Frontal Wave Face Slope

Especially on the frontal wave face, the angle of slope to the horizontal or vertical line (or to the reference line from the primary wave peak to the center hole of the graph, i.e. "obliquity angle") is very similar in the quiet or active state, as shown by Dontas[32],[33] (Figs. B-9, B-10). There was good agreement as to slope, shape, and amplitude between the intra-arterial pulse wave and the extra-arterial pulse wave at 60 mm Hg, or at diastolic pressure level. The frontal slope angle agreed within the 40 to 100 mm Hg range. When the systolic blood pressure was artifically raised, the external pulse wave was reduced in amplitude. Peripheral resistance and variations of tension in the walls of the arteries depress the waves.

In a second study, Dontas compared the volume pulse (electrical impedance method of Nyberg) and the pressure pulse (with Cournand needle), obtaining these simultaneously in thirteen young men. The foot of the volume pulse preceded the pressure by 0.010 seconds at the brachial cuff position and the area was 27.3 percent larger. Amyl nitrite increased the volume pulse. The peak was reached first by the pressure pulse, then the volume pulse, differing by 0.035 seconds to reach the same height, and the overall volume systole exceeded by 0.04 to 0.06 seconds that of the pressure systole, the volume pulse decreasing more slowly. No major differences were observed. Hypertension was associated with "flatter" volume pulses, with the systolic phase lasting longer; the delay in onset

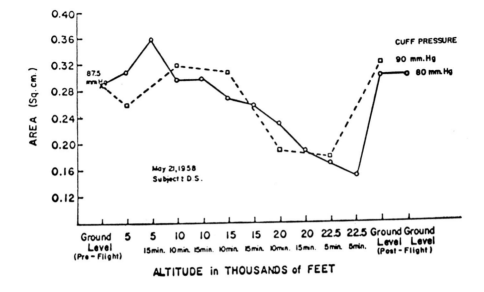

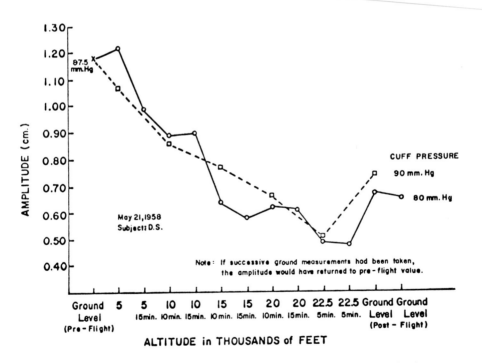

FIGURE B-8. *Top*: Changes in area of heartograph due to changes in altitude. *Bottom*: Changes in systolic amplitude of heartograph due to changes in altitude.

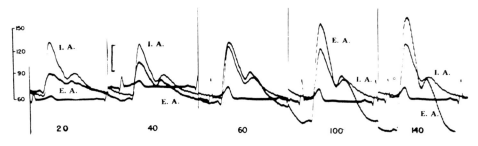

FIGURE B-9. Comparison of externally taken waves with those taken internally. Simultaneous intra-arterial (I.A.) and extra-arterial (E.A.) brachial artery pressure pulses recorded from the same point, with constant gain, but cuff under different pressures; the numbers underneath indicate levels of cuff pressure in mm Hg. In this and in Figure B-10, the pressure levels on the left apply for all intra-arterial pressure pulses. Volume calibration for extra-arterial pulse with 40 mm Hg pressure = 0.25 ml. (From Dontas.)

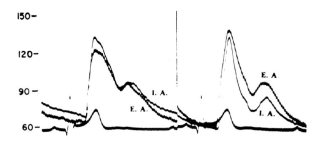

FIGURE B-10. Intra-arterial and extra-arterial pulses (at cuff pressure of 50 mm Hg) of the brachial artery at elbow; the extra-arterial pulses carry a mild 60-cycle interference. *Left*: Control. *Right*: Five seconds after occlusion of circulation to lower arm with a cuff inflated to 300 mm Hg. Observe the similar qualitative but different quantitative response, the extra-arterial pulse becoming the larger and wider of the two. (From Dontas.)

of the pressure pulse got shorter, and occasionally the rise in pressure preceded the rise in volume. The brachial artery responded as a partly distensible elastic tube, whose wall became more rigid in hypertension.

Dontas' work is in essential agreement with other work by Rushmer,[34] Kroeker and Wood,[35] and Heyman[36] in that the externally and internally taken pulses at rest are almost identical in the frontal wave face slope and shape of the initial systolic ejection curve, but some differences were observed in the diastolic recovery phase. Some variations are due to respiration phases. There was also faster return to the base line of the volume pulse during late diastole.

Kroeker and Wood[37] point out that the waves are remarkably similar with two different systems of monitoring: (1) strain gauge manometer system and (2) higher frequency capacitance manometer.

Quantitation of Brachial Pulse Waves

The first quantitation of the brachial pulse wave was reported in Cureton's work of 1947 *(Physical Fitness Appraisal and Guidance)*. Much more work was reported in 1951 *(Physical Fitness of Champion Athletes)*. Figure B-11 shows the quantitation diagram, all principal dimensions were calipered, the area planimetered, and velocity characteristics computed. Correlations were worked out with endurance criteria like the mile run, the all-out treadmill run, and biserial correlations were computed to differentiate the highly trained groups from the untrained, or lesser trained,

TABLE B-I

STANDARD SCORE RATING SCALE FOR HEARTOGRAPH AREA/SURFACE AREA
(Young men, Illinois Medical School Freshmen)

Grade	Heartograph Area SA* (sq cm per sq m)	HGF Area (sq cm)	Letter Grade	Standard Score	Percentile
Superior	.339	.66		100	99.87
	.322	.62	A+	95	99.65
	.305	.59		90	99.18
Very good	.287	.55		85	98.2
	.270	.51	A	80	96.4
	.253	.48		75	93.3
Above average (good)	.236	.44		70	88.4
	.219	.41	B	65	81.6
	.201	.37		60	72.6
Average	.184	.33		55	61.8
	.167	.30	C+	50	50.0
	.150	.26		45	38.2
Below average	.133	.23		40	27.4
	.115	.19	C	35	18.4
	.098	.15		30	11.5
Poor	.081	.12		25	6.7
	.064	.08	D	20	3.6
	.047	.05		15	1.8
Very poor	.029	.01		10	.82
	.012	.005	E	5	.35
	.000	.001	(failing)	0	.14
M	.167	.298			
σ	.0573	.122			
N	110	110			

* SA is surface area of the body taken from the Boothby-Sandiford tables.

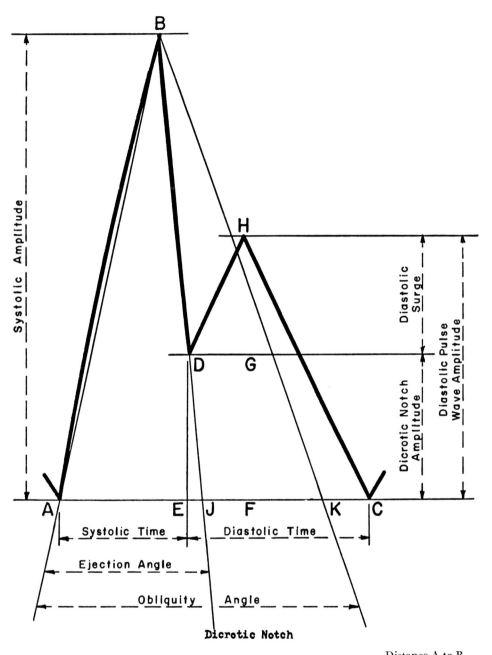

FIGURE B-11. Diagram of normal pulse wave. *Velocity of ejection* $= \dfrac{\text{Distance A to B}}{\text{Time to raise A to B.}}$

Acceleration may be determined from a second derivative electronic circuit. *Note*: Assuming A to B to be a straight line, then a vertical erected at any time point would make a right triangle; the base and amplitude of the right triangle are in direct proportion, so either amplitude or "time of peak" is proportional to velocity. By permission of Cameron Heartometer Corporation.

TABLE B-II

RATING SCALES FOR HEARTOGRAPH ANGLES

	Adult Males				Young Men		
SS	Percentile	Ejection Angle	Obliquity Angle	SS	Percentile	Ejection Angle	Obliquity Angle
100	99.9		14.8	100	99.9		15.6
95	99.6		15.5	95	99.6	0.16	16.2
90	99.2	0.35	16.1	90	99.2	1.33	16.8
85	98.2	1.91	16.8	85	98.2	2.50	17.3
80	96.4	2.47	17.5	80	96.4	3.67	17.9
75	93.3	5.03	18.2	75	93.3	4.84	18.5
70	88.4	6.59	18.8	70	88.4	6.01	19.0
65	81.6	8.15	19.5	65	81.6	7.18	19.6
60	72.6	9.71	20.2	60	72.6	8.35	20.2
55	61.8	11.27	20.8	55	61.8	9.52	20.7
50	50.0	12.83	21.4	50	50.0	10.69	21.3
45	38.2	14.39	22.0	45	38.2	11.86	21.9
40	27.4	15.95	22.8	40	27.4	13.03	22.4
35	18.4	17.51	23.5	35	18.4	14.20	23.0
30	11.5	19.07	24.2	30	11.5	15.37	23.6
25	6.7	20.63	24.8	25	6.7	16.54	24.1
20	3.6	22.19	25.5	20	3.6	17.71	24.7
15	1.8	23.75	26.2	15	1.8	18.88	25.3
10	0.8	25.31	26.9	10	0.8	20.05	25.8
5	0.4	26.87	27.5	5	0.4	21.22	26.4
0	0.1	28.43	28.2	0	0.1	22.39	27.0
M		12.83	21.37			10.69	21.30
σ		5.21	2.24			3.90	1.89
N		420	263			365	365

groups. The data are also shown as bar graphs in terms of means. Reliability coefficients were determined in test and retest work for all measurements.

Normative tables were developed to facilitate comparisons. Three such tables, not included in the other publications, are given here (Tables B-I, B-II, B-III).

In addition to the chapters in the books, Cureton published several interpretative statements on the brachial pulse wave as it became an appreciated and valuable tool in the work of the Physical Fitness Research Laboratory, at the University of Illinois.[38, 39, 40] These supplemented earlier statements by Cureton and Massey.[41] In 1949 it was reported by the former that quiet sitting for 2 hours would reduce the pulse wave area approximately 30 percent in graduate students and that, in a 2-hour lecture, the

TABLE B-III

RATING SCALE FOR HEARTOMETER MEASUREMENTS
AFTER RUNNING IN PLACE 30 STEPS/MIN FOR 1 MIN
(Adult Males, 26-65 Yrs)

	Area Under Curve	Systolic Amplitude	Diastolic Amplitude	Obliquity Angle	Pulse Rate
Excellent	.51	2.41	.80	11.35	35.77
	.48	2.28	.75	12.39	43.26
	.45	2.16	.70	13.42	50.74
Very good	.41	2.03	.65	14.46	58.23
	.38	1.91	.60	15.49	65.71
	.35	1.78	.55	16.53	73.20
Above average	.32	1.65	.50	17.56	80.68
	.29	1.53	.45	18.60	88.17
	.25	1.40	.40	19.63	95.65
Average	.22	1.28	.35	20.67	103.14
	.19	1.15	.30	21.70	111.00
	.16	1.02	.25	22.74	118.11
Below average	.13	.90	.19	23.77	125.59
	.09	.77	.13	24.81	133.08
	.06	.65	.07	25.84	140.56
Poor	.03	.52	.01	26.88	148.04
	.00	.39	.00	27.91	155.53
	.00	.27	.00	28.95	163.02
Very poor	.00	.14	.00	29.98	170.50
	.00	.02	.00	31.02	179.99
	.00	.00	.00	32.05	185.47
Mean	.1945	1.15	.3020	21.72	110.62
σ	.107	.42	.165	3.45	24.95
N	107	107	107	107	107

professor would have his own wave reduced about 50 percent, associated with nervous tension and hard mental activity over such an unbroken period. The amplitude also reduced, and the diastolic surge (rebound wave) disappeared. In several studies this has been identified as being the result of nervous tension and increased total peripheral resistance. It was found, by contrast, that endurance training programs increased all of the same dimensions associated with awakening the blood flow. Men were shown to lose amplitude in the pulse wave when taken to simulated altitudes of 5,000; 10,000; 15,000; and 20,000 feet in a decompression chamber. But if they breathed forced oxygen, the waves were restored partly to their initial status, and after decompression to normal barometric pressure for 15 to 30 minutes, they were fully restored.

Massey-Cureton-Strydom-Fox-MacLeay Experiment, Relating Pulse Waves to Cardiac Output

Figures B-12 and B-13 show a subject being tested on brachial pulse waves while he pedals a bicycle, the bicycle with a chair seat with a back substituted for the usual seat. This was to permit a firm back support while pedalling at increased velocity. The pulse waves (Massey-Cureton-Strydom-Fox-MacLeay experiment) were measured two days: (1) by the Johnson oscillometer with optical recording, which is the instrument with

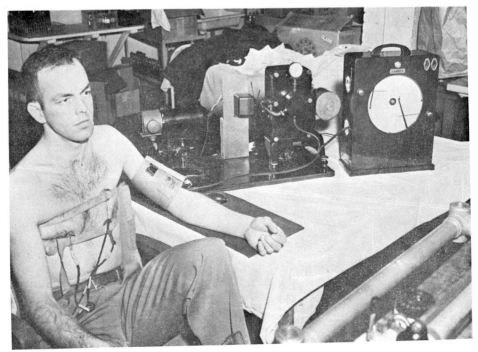

FIGURE B-12.

a "bubble in capillary tube" with optical light closest to the subject and (2) by the heartometer shown at the right. The latter was used on one arm, while the Johnson oscillometer was picked up from the other arm. At rest, and then at four other higher rates of pedalling, the oxygen intake was obtained while the subject was at rest or pedalling. The Grollman, acetylene rebreathing system was also used to permit obtaining the oxygen arteriovenous differences each time. Blood samples were also taken. Figure B-14 shows the four work loads (3537, 5791, 7640 and 8942 ft lbs per min) and the corresponding white cell corpuscular count taken at each load after the ride was steadily on for 2 minutes. The brachial pulse waves taken with the heartometer and oscillometer were in good agreement as shown in Massey's study. The significant observation was that the amplitude of the brachial pulse waves were proportionately higher at each work load, as shown in Figures B-15, B-16, B-17 on the three subjects used in the experiment.

The Erlanger-Hooker (Pulse Pressure × Pulse Rate) is shown as related in straight line proportionate fashion to the heart minute volume (Fig. B-18). The minute volume increased with the progressive work loads and was

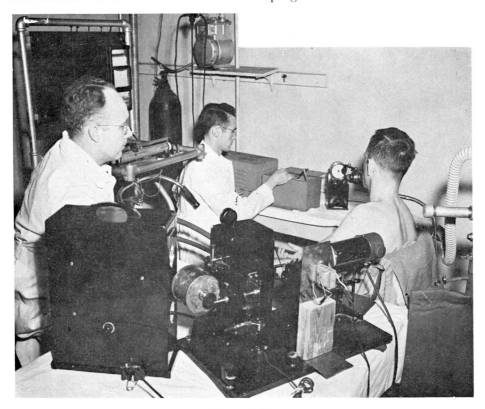

FIGURE B-13.

(Fig. B-19) shown to be fairly proportional to pulse rate except at the higher work load (Fig. B-20). The minute volume was also quite proportional to the Tigerstedt Index, the ratio of the pulse pressure per systolic pressure (Fig. B-21), and also to the Barach Index

$$\frac{\text{(Diastolic pressure plus systolic pressure}}{100} \times \text{pulse rate)}$$

(Fig. B-22). The systolic amplitude is shown related proportionately to the "rate of rise" determined by measuring the heartometer waves (Fig. B-23). Both heartometer and oscillometer amplitudes were highly related to stroke volume (Fig. B-24) and to oxygen intake (Fig. B-25).

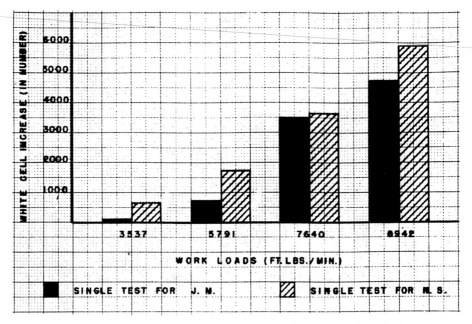

FIGURE B-14. White cell count increase with progressive work loads. Physical Fitness Research Laboratory, U. of Ill.

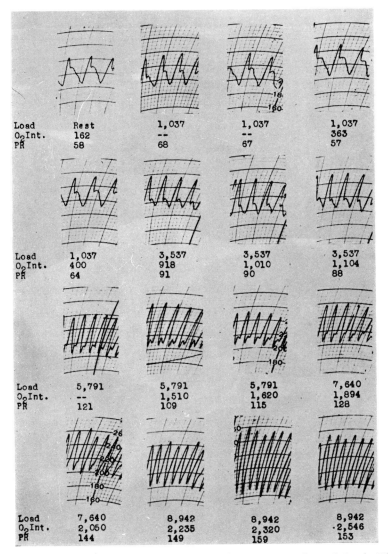

FIGURE B-15. The heartometer pulse waves of subject N.S. at each work load. The pulse rate (PR) in beats per minute, oxygen intake (O₂ Int.) in cc per minute, and work load in foot pounds per minute are recorded below the respective waves.

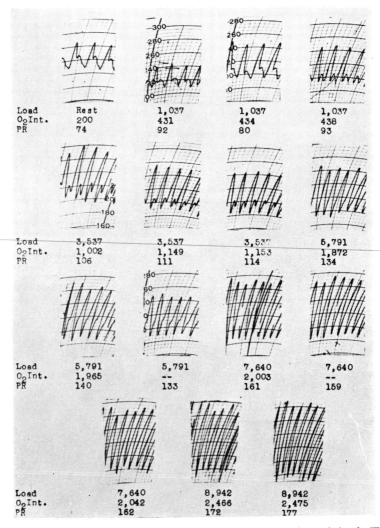

Load	Rest	1,037	1,037	1,037
O_2Int.	200	431	434	438
PR	74	92	80	93

Load	3,537	3,537	3,537	5,791
O_2Int.	1,002	1,149	1,153	1,872
PR	106	111	114	134

Load	5,791	5,791	7,640	7,640
O_2Int.	1,965	--	2,003	--
PR	140	133	161	159

Load	7,640	8,942	8,942
O_2Int.	2,042	2,466	2,475
PR	162	172	177

FIGURE B-16.   The heartometer pulse waves of subject J.M. at each work load. The pulse rate, oxygen intake, and work load are recorded below the respective waves.

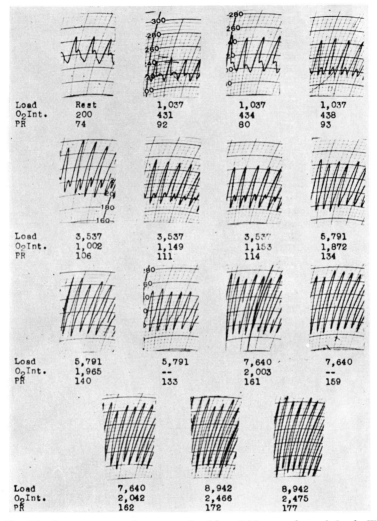

Load	Rest	1,037	1,037	1,037
O$_2$Int.	200	431	434	438
PR	74	92	80	93

Load	3,537	3,537	3,537	5,791
O$_2$Int.	1,002	1,149	1,153	1,872
PR	106	111	114	134

Load	5,791	5,791	7,640	7,640
O$_2$Int.	1,965	--	2,003	--
PR	140	133	161	159

Load	7,640	8,942	8,942
O$_2$Int.	2,042	2,466	2,475
PR	162	172	177

FIGURE B-17. The heartometer pulse waves of subject J.M. at each work load. The pulse rate, oxygen intake, and work load are recorded below the respective waves.

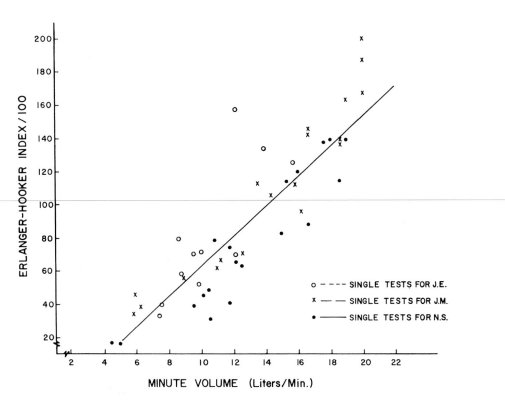

ERLANGER-HOOKER INDEX = PULSE PRESSURE x PULSE RATE

FIGURE B-18.   Relationship between Erlanger-Hooker Index and heart minute volume during exercise. Physical Fitness Research Laboratory, U. of Ill.

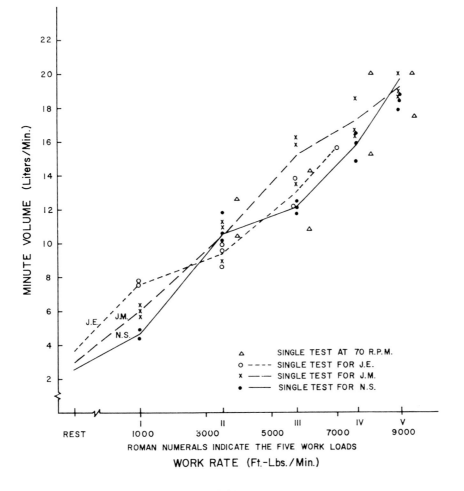

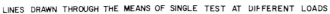
LINES DRAWN THROUGH THE MEANS OF SINGLE TEST AT DIFFERENT LOADS

FIGURE B-19. Changes in minute volume of the heart with progressive work loads. Physical Fitness Research Laboratory, U. of Ill.

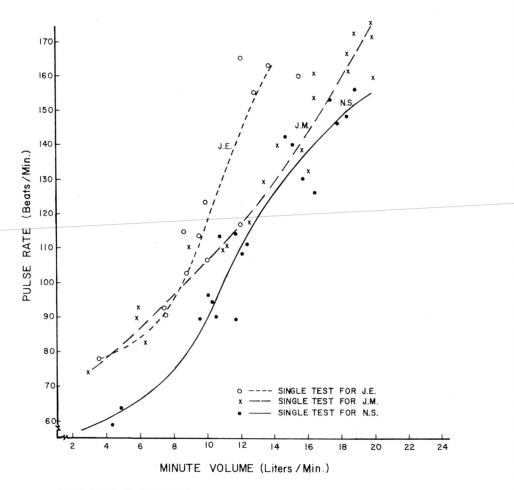

LINES DRAWN BY INSPECTION

FIGURE B-20. Heart minute volume and pulse rate. Physical Fitness Research Laboratory, U. of Ill.

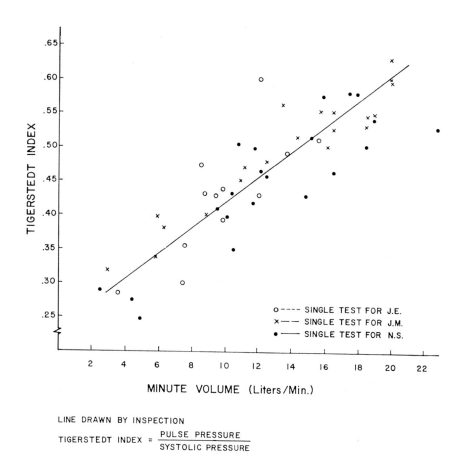

FIGURE B-21. The relation between heart minute volume and Tigerstedt Index. Physical Fitness Research Laboratory, U. of Ill.

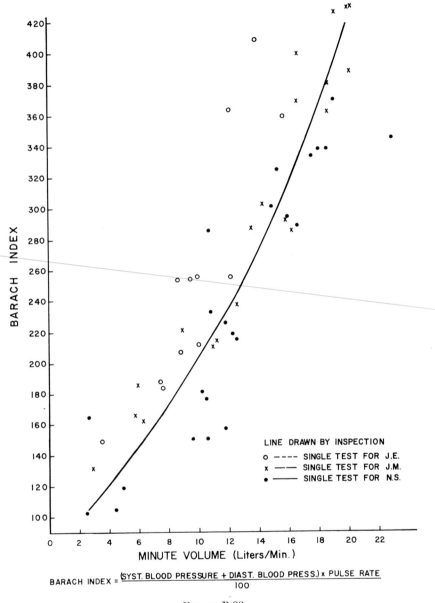

FIGURE B-22.

HEARTOMETER AND OSCILLOMETER SYSTOLIC AMPLITUDES
RELATED TO RATE OF SYSTOLIC RISE

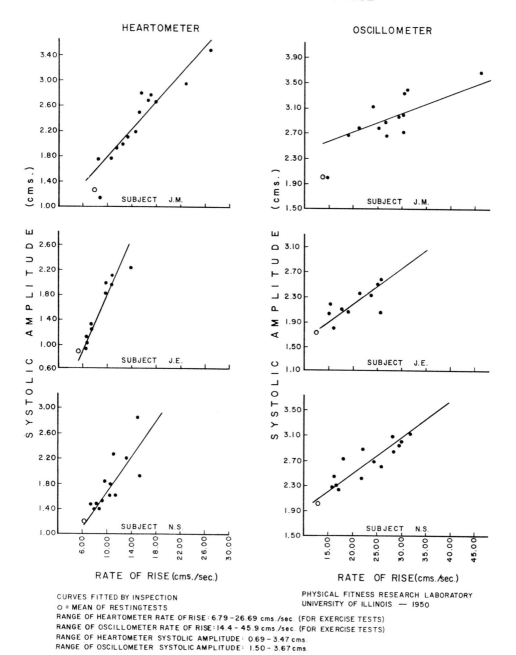

HEARTOMETER

OSCILLOMETER

SYSTOLIC AMPLITUDE (cms.)

SUBJECT J.M.

SUBJECT J.E.

SUBJECT N.S.

RATE OF RISE (cms./sec.)

CURVES FITTED BY INSPECTION
O = MEAN OF RESTINGTESTS
RANGE OF HEARTOMETER RATE OF RISE: 6.79 – 26.69 cms./sec. (FOR EXERCISE TESTS)
RANGE OF OSCILLOMETER RATE OF RISE: 14.4 – 45.9 cms./sec. (FOR EXERCISE TESTS)
RANGE OF HEARTOMETER SYSTOLIC AMPLITUDE: 0.69 – 3.47 cms.
RANGE OF OSCILLOMETER SYSTOLIC AMPLITUDE: 1.50 – 3.67 cms.

PHYSICAL FITNESS RESEARCH LABORATORY
UNIVERSITY OF ILLINOIS — 1950

FIGURE B-23.

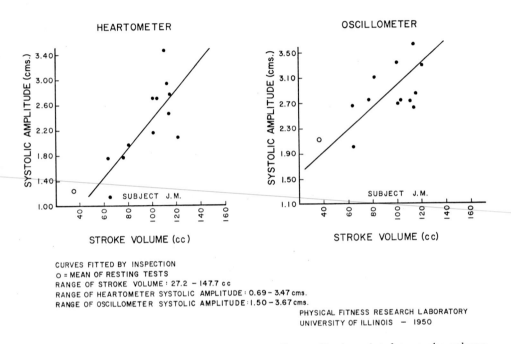

CURVES FITTED BY INSPECTION
O = MEAN OF RESTING TESTS
RANGE OF STROKE VOLUME : 27.2 – 147.7 cc
RANGE OF HEARTOMETER SYSTOLIC AMPLITUDE : 0.69 – 3.47 cms.
RANGE OF OSCILLOMETER SYSTOLIC AMPLITUDE : 1.50 – 3.67 cms.

PHYSICAL FITNESS RESEARCH LABORATORY
UNIVERSITY OF ILLINOIS — 1950

FIGURE B-24.   Heartometer and oscillometer systolic amplitudes related to stroke volume.

HEARTOMETER AND OSCILLOMETER SYSTOLIC AMPLITUDES
RELATED TO OXYGEN INTAKE PER MINUTE

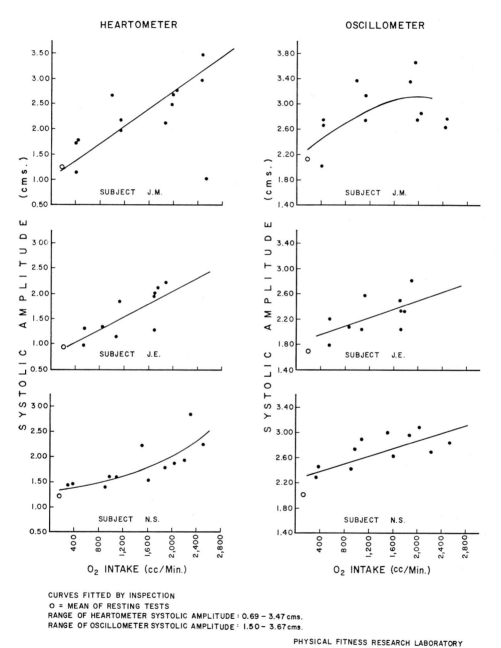

CURVES FITTED BY INSPECTION
O = MEAN OF RESTING TESTS
RANGE OF HEARTOMETER SYSTOLIC AMPLITUDE : 0.69 – 3.47 cms.
RANGE OF OSCILLOMETER SYSTOLIC AMPLITUDE : 1.50 – 3.67 cms.

PHYSICAL FITNESS RESEARCH LABORATORY
UNIVERSITY OF ILLINOIS — 1950

FIGURE B-25. Heartometer and oscillometer systolic amplitudes related to oxygen intake per minute.

Relations to Stroke Volume, Minute Volume, and Oxygen Intake

A number of experiments show that the brachial pulse waves, if properly taken to obtain the "optimum" wave 10 to 15 mm Hg above the diastolic level, are highly related to the stroke volume and blood flow through the heart. In two correlated experiments, Massey[42] and Strydom[43] demonstrated in four progressive levels of work that the amplitudes were proportional to stroke volume. The Grollman method was used (acetylene rebreathing) while the subjects pedalled an ergometer bicycle (Fig. B-12). Massey compared the heartometer pulse waves with the Johnson oscillator waves. Both had "overshoot" nearly alike, but the changes in the waves with different levels of work were quite proportional. Fox[44] determined the periodic frequency of the heartometer to be 3.5 cycles per second. He also measured the comparative sensitivity and found the Johnson (frictionless capillary bubble-in-tube) to be just slightly better than the heartometer, but there was little difference. The friction lag in the heartometer is remarkably low, due to the relatively frictionless bellows, the vertical suspension of the writing pen, and ingenious methods used to reduce friction. The amplitudes in the four stages of work were found to be proportional to the stroke volume (Figs. B-15, B-16, B-17). However, the areas were not useful when the pulse rate went over 100 beats per minute, these losing shape on the diastolic side of the wave. The amplitudes in the four levels of work were highly related to oxygen intake and to minute volume.

Michael-Cureton Studies Relating Brachial Pulse Waves to Cardiac Output and Stroke Volume

Using the Grollman method to determine stroke volume, Michael[45] found a high relationship between the heartometer wave amplitude and stroke volume as determined in twenty-one young men. The relationship was rectilinear at rest, but the values were low by 38 cc, as estimated by Cureton, when comparing the slope with age lines of Landowne, Brandfonbrenner, and Shock with plots of Michael's data. Figure B-26 shows this relationship, with 38 cc being an average correction within the 20-to-50-year range. Since this correction is a constant error type, it does not affect the correlational relations reported in the statistical treatments. Its use puts the heartograph values approximately to the level of the catheterization and Stewart dye results. At the National Institute of Health, Gerontological Branch, Lansdowne, Brandfonbrenner, and Shock[46] found that the heart pumped 1 percent per year less blood after age 30. This reduction was attributed to the steadily increasing total peripheral resistance (TPR).

In general, our findings on the value of the heartograph at the Physical Fitness Research Laboratory corresponded to the findings reported by Kar-

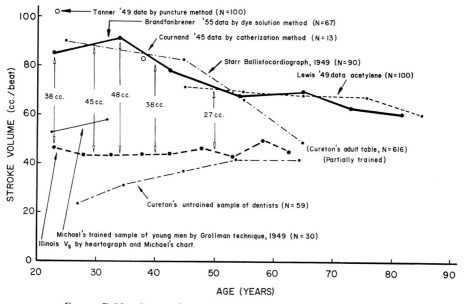

FIGURE B-26. Comparison of stroke volume by various methods.

vonen[47] who described the best hearts as those which could increase their output per beat or per minute the most in response to athletic performance demands, and this also paralleled by a large maximal aerobic oxygen intake. The results are conditioned by the amount of tension in the muscles, the volume of respiration, and the trained experience in the nervous system of the subject. Values were different for the same subject in comparisons on the bicycle, the treadmill, and in the pool.

In further work, using the Grollman method on young men at ground level and in the decompression chamber, Michael and Cureton[48] found that a systematic endurance training program increased the stroke volume and cardiac output in tests at ground level and at altitude with subjects in the sitting position.

Wang, Marshall, and Shepherd[49] reported that position was important, comparing supine to vertical positions, and found in walking $4\frac{1}{2}$ miles per hour on the treadmill at 12° grade, that the stroke output was 59 cc per beat compared to 32 at rest while standing still, and was 54 at rest in the supine position. An editorial in *Circulation* (March 1960) points out that the conflicting data in this area are due to test data being taken in different positions.

Effect of Venous Impedance Upon Brachial Pulse Wave

Wren[50] applied a tourniquet to the left thighs of twenty-one male college students (130 mm Hg for 30 seconds) and took the brachial pulse wave both before and just afterward in various positions. There was marked

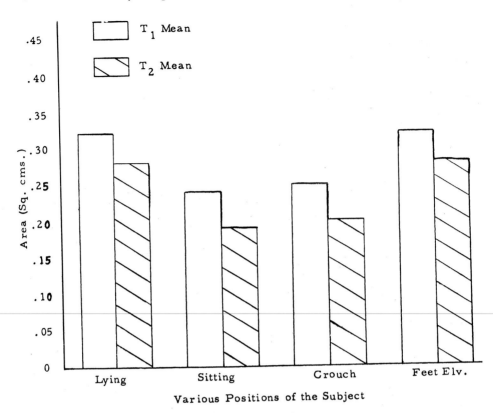

FIGURE B-27. Brachial pulse wave changes in area as affected by venous impedance.

reduction in the area under the brachial pulse wave and also loss of amplitude. This experiment clearly shows that the pulse wave reflects circulation and is very much affected by the blood returning to the heart. Since more blood returning means more blood ejected, the test should be viewed as a circulatory test (Fig. B-27).

Posture itself may be a type of venous impedance since the "sag" in the blood while standing (as reflected in Crampton's Blood Ptosis Test) is also a cause usually of lowered pulse pressure. We have long used the difference between the amplitude of the brachial pulse wave sitting and standing as an indicator of the efficiency of the venous return circulation. Cureton[51] has published tables for this "decrement pulse wave test" along with tables for drops in pulse pressure, these to supplement Crampton's Test.

Massey, Husman, and Kehoe[52] found the decrement between the sitting and standing brachial pulse wave in seventy young men, 17 to 27 years of age, to be a good predictive index for the 880-yard run, the fitter subjects by the pulse wave decrement test having *less* decrement and better time. The initial sitting systolic amplitude divided by surface area of the body gave the best biserial correlation to separate the "good" from the "poor" running groups ($r_{bis.} = 0.799$). The highest t-ratio and mean differences were for the change in the systolic amplitude, lying to standing ($t = 8.70$). Cureton, Adams, and others have shown the amplitude of the brachial pulse wave to be as good after running 1 minute in place, 180 steps per minute.

Effect of Physical Training Upon Stroke Volume and Brachial Pulse Wave

Figures B-28 and B-29 show the results of the Michael-Cureton Track Training Program, in which the stroke volume changes were measured concomitantly with the brachial pulse waves on male graduate students, 24 to 30 years of age. In the first 12 weeks from T_1 to T_2, the amplitude of the brachial pulse wave increased from 1.74 to 1.91 cm in the ground level tests. Changes were paralleled by similar increases in stroke volume, and the increases as measured at 10,000 feet of simulated altitude were from 1.21 to 1.50 cm. Then, after 12 weeks, there was a leveling off and some slight reduction (adaptation?) in the next six weeks, T_2 to T_3. These changes were paralleled in the Grollman stroke volume results, which values increased 36.6 percent at ground level (T_1 to T_2) and 26 percent at altitude in the same period of training for 12 weeks.

The above work corroborates in principle the work on dogs of Warner[53] and of Huggins and Smith,[54] who demonstrated that the brachial pulse contour method gave data which were essentially rectilinear and highly related to the direct Fick method within 8 percent. These works and that of Swan *et al.*[55] corroborate the principle that the quantitation of the brachial arterial waves may closely approximate the stroke volume in the quiet state.

Cureton determined that the systolic amplitude of the Cameron heartometer brachial pulse waves was highly correlated with oxygen intake in the all-out treadmill run, 7 miles per hour, 8.6 percent grade (Fig. B-30).

Jones, Hefner, Bancroft, and Chip,[56] working on dogs, measured the continuous blood flow velocity by a single-lumen catheter, using a Navier-Stokes equation and an electronic computer to solve the equation. From the area under the velocity curve, the cardiac output was determined, and this was compared with the cardiac output as measured by the simultaneous dye-dilution technique. The correlation was 0.97.

M. P. Spencer, F. R. Johnson, and A. B. Denison[57] reported that the form of the aortic flow pulse, as measured by an electroflow meter, was affected by "inertiance" and "compliance" of the aortic arterial tree, and the cardiac ejection pulse excited heavily damped resonance of 3 to 6 cycles per second.

At the Mayo Clinic Graduate School of Medicine, John C. P. Williams and Earl H. Wood[58] reported "on the line" computer analysis of the central

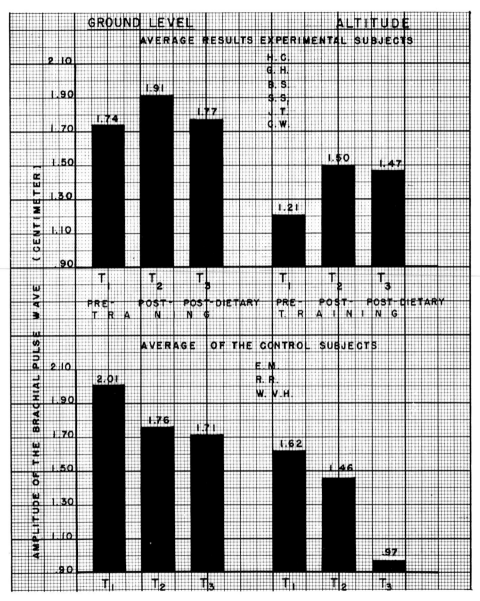

FIGURE B-28.   Effects of training on systolic amplitude of brachial pulse wave. Michael-Cureton Track Training Program.

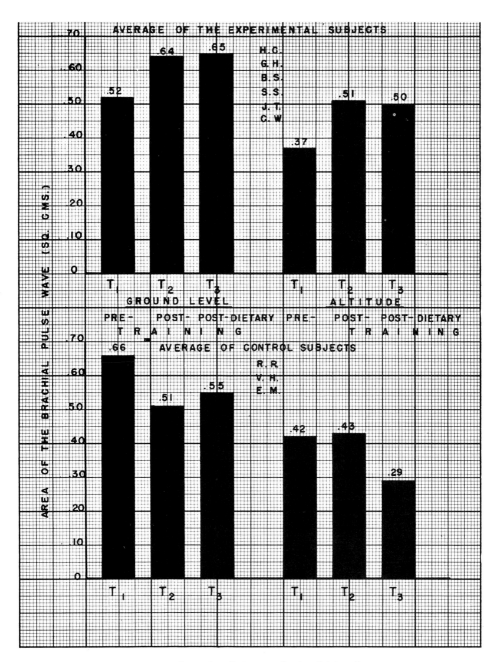

FIGURE B-29. Effect of training on the brachial pulse wave.

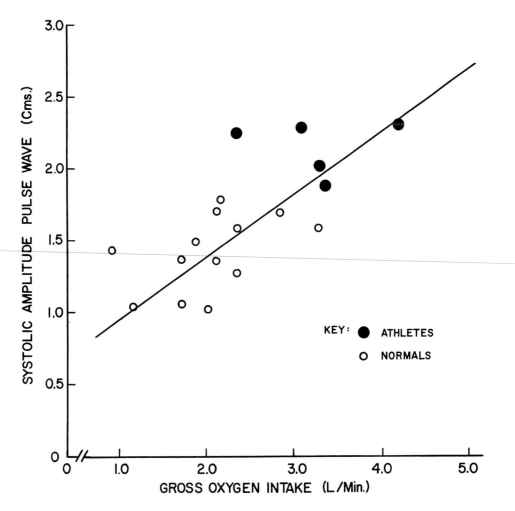

FIGURE B-30. Gross oxygen intake during all-out treadmill run related to systolic amplitude of brachial pulse wave at rest.

arterial pulse waves with pulse rate controlled, and the arteriovenous (A-V) delay was systematically varied throughout the cardiac cycle. Stroke volume, mean systolic pressure, and resistance were determined by computer analysis. Stroke volume was 80 to 90 percent of maximum when A-V delay was 0.083 and heart rate 90 to 120. Vagal stimulation had little or no effect upon the optimal A-V delay.

In recent years there have been several sophisticated analyses on humans by Brown, Bunnell, and Greene,[59] who recorded the typical initial peak, dicrotic notch, a second peak on the catacrotic limb and a dicrotic wave. Valsalva and epinephrine effects produced elevated waves with extra pressure, and it was conversely concluded that stroke volume and total peripheral resistance affected the waves.

J. E. Kendrick[60] concluded that an increased pulse frequency and decreased stroke volume decreased all harmonics.

Freis, Lucksinger, Snell, and Heath[61] concluded after studying the carotid pulse with modern electronic procedures, that drugs (isoproterenol and amyl nitrite) which increase stroke volume and decrease total peripheral resistance markedly increased the first peak of the carotid pulse, the velocity (amplitude) and stroke volume, and conversely for the effect of depressive drugs (angiotensin and methoxamine). They concluded that high systolic pressure and loss of arterial distensibility decreased the first peak of the wave.

Cureton[62] made a logical analysis of the major components in a complex battery of cardiovascular tests by analyzing several factor analyses of various workers. Errors in logic were shown wherein several workers had attempted to validate one cardiovascular component against another of a very different nature.

Factor Analysis Studies

In a comprehensive factor analysis of 104 cardiovascular variables, Cureton and Sterling[63] reported that the amplitude of the heartograph came out first with the greatest percent of total variance compared to various other factors. In a correlative study, but which used Cattell's P-technique,[64] the BCG waves came out first and the heartograph waves second. Then came oxygen requirement, pulse pressure after running all-out, weight, low pulse rates in recuperation, gross oxygen (aerobic) intake, and slow quiet (standing, sitting, or lying) pulse rate.

Parallel Interpretations of Ballistocardiogram and Heartograph

Starr and Ogawa[65] have likened the simple displacement wave (AREA) to the cardiac output (mileage), the amplitude to the velocity (cardiac energy), and the slope on the wave face to acceleration (cardiac force) (Fig. B-31).

The logical analysis indicates to us that in the heartograph, the Newtonian formula for impulse (Ft = Mv) is applicable where F and V are pro-

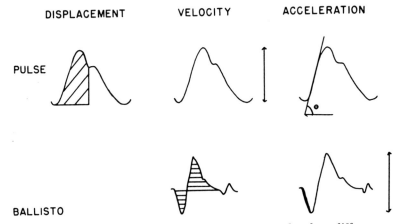

TOTAL FORCE OR ENERGY =

$$A X \quad + \quad B X' \quad + \quad C X''$$

DISPLACEMENT	VELOCITY	ACCELERATION

FOR YOUR AUTO

MILEAGE METER	SPEEDOMETER	ACCELEROMETER

FOR YOUR HEART

CARDIAC OUTPUT	CARDIAC WORK	CARDIAC FORCE
	FRICTION	(F = MA)
	KINETIC ENERGY	
	POTENTIAL ENERGY	
	PULSE	BALLISTO

FIGURE 31a. The "force" of "energy" equation. Standard differential equation used by physicists to describe the important aspects of moving objects. The relation of the three aspects of movement represented by the equation, to familiar aspects of the performance of automobiles and to cardiac performance, is also indicated. Pulse and ballisto are placed under the aspects of cardiac performance which their amplitude represents, the latter with certain reservations. (After Starr and Ogawa.)

ASPECTS OF CARDIAC FUNCTION

	DISPLACEMENT	VELOCITY	ACCELERATION
PULSE			
BALLISTO			

FIGURE B-31b. Different aspects of pulse and ballisto are related to different aspects of cardiac function. Thus, pulse amplitude is placed under the velocity aspects of cardiac function; pulse area, under displacement; pulse slope, under acceleration. If ballisto amplitude is placed under acceleration, ballisto should be placed under velocity, and so forth. The HI segment, that part of the ballisto record which is the "purest" record of cardiac forces, is represented by a thicker line. (After Starr and Ogawa.[65])

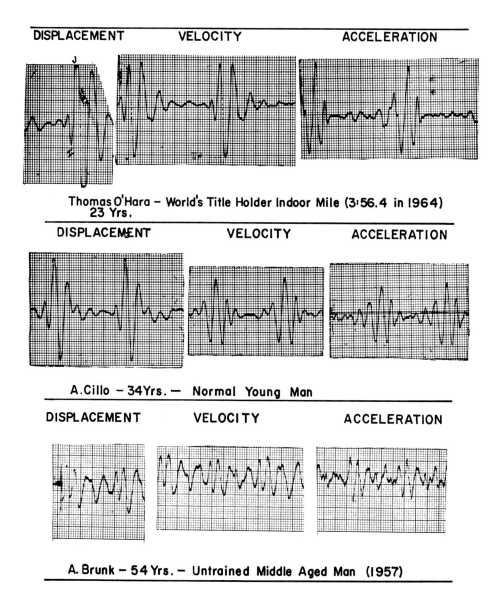

FIGURE B-32. Comparison of BCG's of a highly trained athlete with an untrained young man and an unfit middle-aged man.

portions for a given rate or time of ejection of a given M (mass) of blood. In the BCG, neglecting friction, the formula for accelerated motion ($F = Ma$) is applicable but more exactly in the Ballisticor (ULF) type of machine.

Figure B-32 shows the strong, sharp, regular waves from the Arbeit direct body BCG and also the good ones of a relatively fit young man, compared to the irregular and weak tracing of a 54-year-old, relatively unfit man (AB). Such BCG's compare similarly with heartographs as shown in Figures B-6 through B-11.

Rushmer[66] has also brought focus upon the "initial impulse" as a most important aspect of the strong, functional heart. Such a strong impulse is the result of adequate stimulation to a well-nutrified and well-trained heart.

Heartograph Validity to Predict Endurance

The heartometer brachial pulse waves correlated with all-out running time on the treadmill (0.60), corrected for curvilinearity (0.72), and also corrected for attenuation (0.80). Electronically taken pulse waves by Banister and Cureton obtained a correlation of 0.74 with mile run time.

Figures B-33 and B-34 show that the data for predicting the treadmill run time are curvilinear, so the rectilinear plot gives a lower Pearson correlation than the coefficient of curvilinear correlation, and so forth. The area of the heartograph divided by surface area of the body was used for this prediction.

Banister, Cureton, Abbott, and Pollard[67] demonstrated that the "time to rise" in the brachial pulse wave correlated 0.72 with the time for the mile run, a faster time being related to a taller and more "inotropic" wave resulting from sympatho-adrenergic stimulation.

Pulse Wave Changes in a Girl Swimmer

Figure B-35 shows changes due to strenuous physical conditioning composed of walking 4 to 5 miles per day plus medicine ball, pulley-work for arms, flutter kicks, side leg-raisings, squat jumps and running-in-place alternately. During the winter school months, the subject swam repetitious 100's slow to fast twice per week, and on weekends she jogged several miles and added more and more pick-ups. Every year for 2 years her brachial pulse waves were stronger until in 1956 she placed in two Olympic finals; from 1956 to 1958 she took 17 of the 21 National swimming records in Canada. In 1960 she tried a comeback for the Rome Olympics but picked up an intestinal upset and did not do as well. She went out of training after the games, and the pulse waves reverted to their untrained state. She tried again to regain form and in 1962 represented Canada in the British Empire Games in Vancouver, but without bettering her peak times. The pulse waves truly reflected her relative "intraining" and "out-of-training" states, just as the records of Carlile do (*cf.* p. 48).

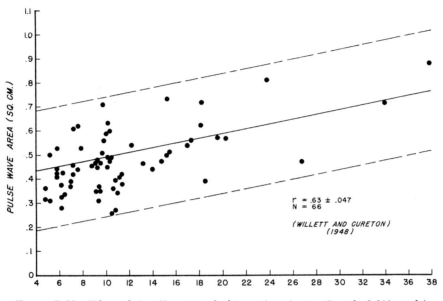

FIGURE B-33. Time of the all-out treadmill run in minutes (7 mph, 8.6% grade).

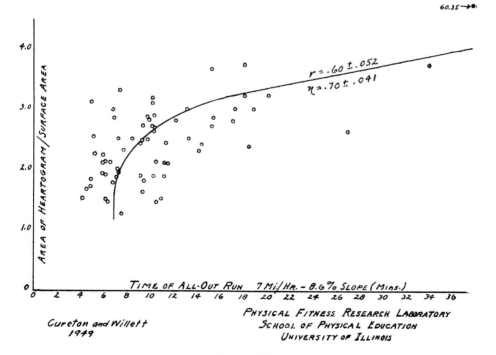

FIGURE B-34.

CHANGES IN SARA BARBER'S BRACHIAL PULSE WAVE

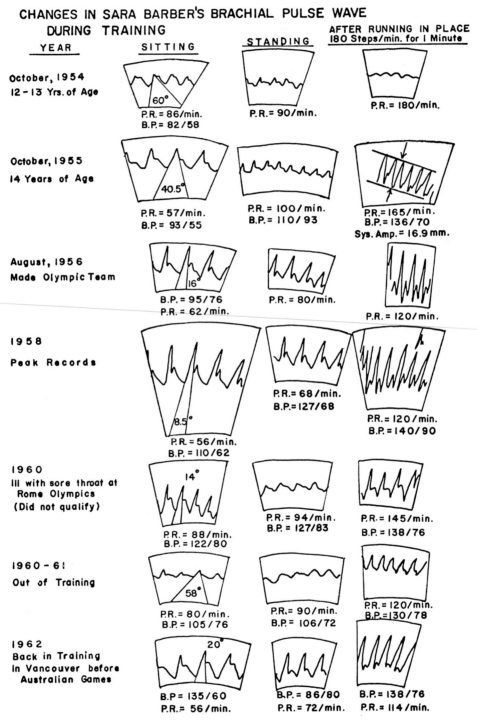

FIGURE B-35.

Trained Endurance Athletes Have Tall, Sharp, High-velocity Ejection Waves

It has long been observed that well-trained endurance athletes in all sports have, at rest, unusually tall, sharp (acute angled) brachial pulse waves in the anacrotic initial impulse (wave face). This is usually called the primary spike. They also have a pronounced secondary spike (diastolic surge) due to resonance rebound from an elastic aortic tree. More tone in the arteries of the aortic tree seems to increase both waves, and they are highly correlated. The intercorrelation matrix is given in the author's *Physical Fitness of Champion Athletes*,[68] along with many examples of such highly trained athletes with the pulse waves reproduced in true size.[69] These waves, taken with a cuff on the arm by means of the Cameron heartometer, are highly related to the large IJ waves of the BCG. This shows in our own work (Liverman and Cureton, Figs. B-46 and B-47), and there is also parallelism with the precordial T-waves and gross O_2 intake (Fig. B-00). Jokl and Wells[70] called specific attention to this similarity in trend, but commensurate units must be used, i.e., velocity vs. velocity.

In Cureton's extensive data, extending over 20 years with measures of several thousand different persons, it is clear that training increases the sizes of these waves. Many groups of known relative endurance were compared. The waves are probably higher because of the increased level of sympathetic nervous stimulation, as the athletes reported by Cureton were in their highest state of training. The vertical dimension, the systolic amplitude, is increased in association with such measures as pulse pressure, systolic blood pressure, basal metabolism, precordial T-waves, and endurance as shown in many training experiments. (Refer to Table V in text where this is clearly shown in Du Toit's data.) The calculation of the Erlanger-Hooker Index indicates that the minute volume of circulation is greater in the systemic circuit. From the measurements one might conclude that both the parasympathetic tuning (slower pulse rate) and sympathetic tuning have occurred. The increased amplitude (and velocity of ejection) is a reflection of the increased sympatho-adrenergic effect, and the increased area is attributable principally to a slower heart rate, usually called parasympathetic but to which there are some known exceptions.[71, 72]

Cureton has shown (Fig. B-5) the successive variations in the brachial pulse wave under several conditions:

1. Normal quiet sitting state (mentally at ease).
2. After a psychological challenge to run a 4-mile race with some young men (20 years younger) (sympathetically stimulated).
3. Immediately after the 4-mile race (sympathetically stimulated).
4 through 7. Successive stages of recovery.

Nickerson reported that the adrenergic catecholamines are of major

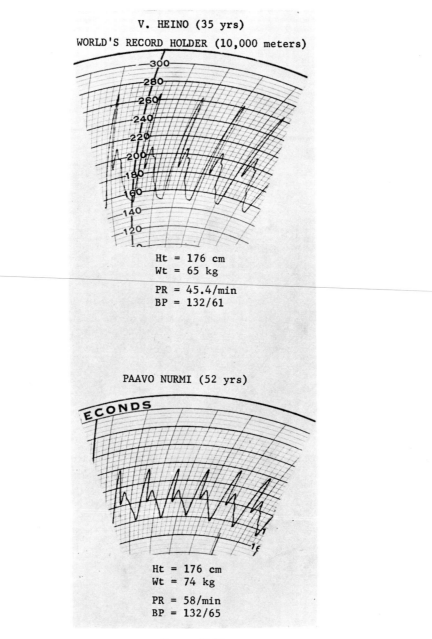

Ht = 176 cm
Wt = 65 kg

PR = 45.4/min
BP = 132/61

PAAVO NURMI (52 yrs)

Ht = 176 cm
Wt = 74 kg

PR = 58/min
BP = 132/65

FIGURE B-36.

JON HENDRICKS

WORLD'S CHAMPION

Melbourne Olympics (100 meters)

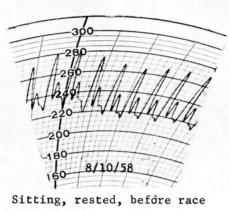

Sitting, rested, before race

PR = 96/min
BP = 122/69

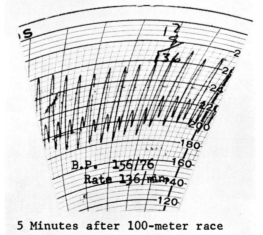

5 Minutes after 100-meter race

FIGURE B-37.

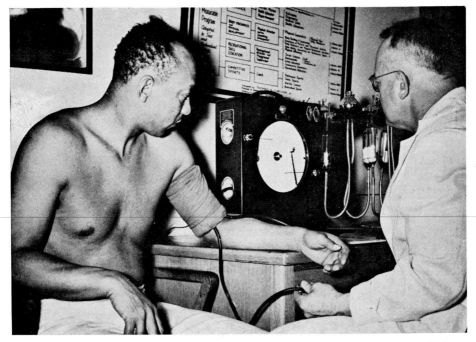

FIGURE B-38.   Jesse Owens, former athlete, 40 years of age, takes heartometer test at Urbana.

FIGURES B-36 through B-39.   Heartograms of great athletes.

FIGURES B-40 through B-42.   Former athletes in good or very good condition.

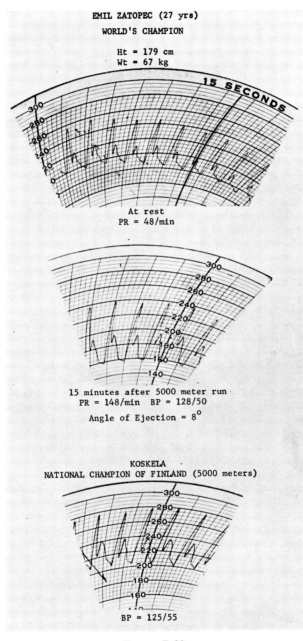

FIGURE B-39.

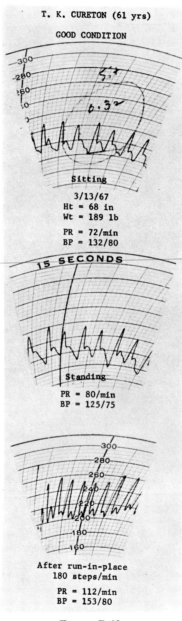

FIGURE B-40.

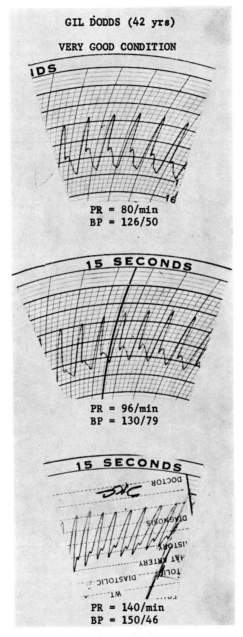

GIL DODDS (42 yrs)

VERY GOOD CONDITION

PR = 80/min
BP = 126/50

15 SECONDS

PR = 96/min
BP = 130/79

15 SECONDS

PR = 140/min
BP = 150/46

FIGURE B-41.

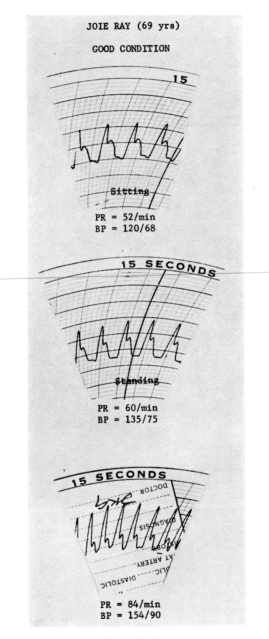

FIGURE B-42.

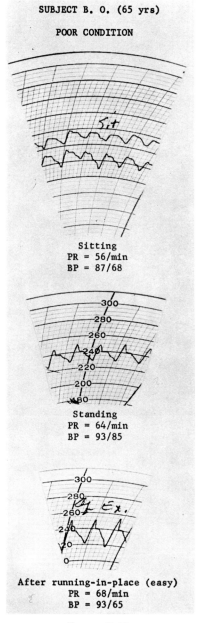

FIGURE B-43.

importance in augmenting heart action in exercise. In our own laboratory we experimented (Dr. John Holloszy) by injecting adrenaline into the veins of several subjects. It is clearly seen that there resulted in a few minutes this augmentor action (Fig. B-5). This is undoubtedly the principal reason why mentally and physically stimulated athletes typically show the tall, sharp brachial pulse waves.[73] Reference should be made to our data on Heusner: in 7 months, his brachial pulse waves increased progressively as the stress of the training continued month after month until he made the best time; then the pulse wave decreased promptly after the training program was stopped. Throughout this progressive training, Heusner showed steadily increasing eosinopenia until the training terminated at the end of the 7 months.

Improvements in Brachial Pulse with Training
(Kristufek-Cureton Experiment)

Many training experiments were carried out at the University of Illinois under Cureton's supervision. Most of these experiments used: (1) the area under the wave, (2) the systolic amplitude, (3) the diastolic surge. All of these were correlated significantly with endurance. The decrement test was added (i.e., a comparison of the sitting with the standing wave). Then a third variation was added to the others, namely, the wave after a brisk run-in-place for 1 minute at 180 steps per minute with the feet lifted at least 4 inches from the floor. Figure B-44 shows the Kristufek-Cureton experiment of the results of a graduate student running 3 miles per day for 5 days per week for 6 weeks.[74] The brachial pulse wave improved markedly, and this was paralleled by improvements in oxygen intake capacity in the all-out treadmill run, 7 miles per hour, 8.6 percent grade.

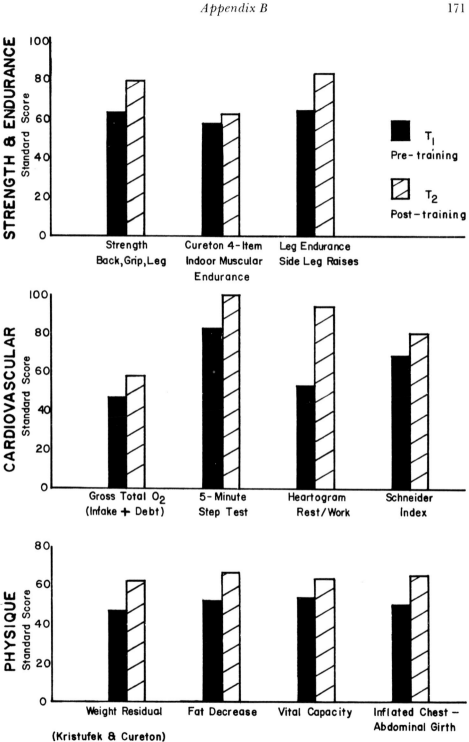

FIGURE B-44. Effects of endurance training on an adult male (3 miles nonstop running each day for 6 weeks).

Jogging and Step Test with O_2 Intake and Debt Determinations

Cureton ran 3 miles per day, 6 days per week, progressing a bit faster after the first week. Figure B-45 shows the improvements, week by week, in the amplitude and area of the brachial pulse wave. In the third week, a definite "diastolic surge" appeared along with a sharp drop in the dicrotic notch. Since the weekly 5-minute step test was a submaximal test for the subject, who was in fairly good condition, the O_2 intake test and energy cost declined, showing the use of less aerobic oxygen for the same work (150 steps up and down on a 14-inch bench) done every Friday afternoon for 5 weeks. The lying, sitting, and standing pulse rates declined sharply in the last three weeks, while the Schneider and Harvard Step Test scores improved. The T-wave dropped in the last week when fastest times were made, showing some after-fatigue and, perhaps, some glycogen and potassium depletion from the heart muscle.

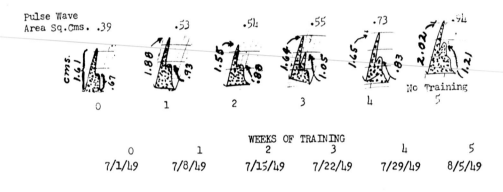

HARD ENDURANCE RUNNING AND SWIMMING

FIGURE B-45. Concomitant changes in peripheral pulse wave and other physical fitness tests during 4 weeks of training.

Experiments Conducted by Graduate Students

Basketball Training	N. L. LaBaw	M.S., 1951
	C. D. Fulton	M.S., 1951
Football Training	E. C. Anderson	M.S., 1950
Wrestling	R. L. Ryan	M.S., 1961
Handball	F. O. Bryant	M.S., 1950
Volleyball	C. P. Wolbers	M.S., 1950
Weight Lifting	M. E. Brodt	M.S., 1950
	A. L. Wilson	M.S., 1946
Adult Swimming	A. B. Harrison	M.S., 1950
Swimming Training	P. K. Nakamura	M.S., 1951
	R. H. Pohndorf	Ph.D., 1957
	M. H. Kong	M.S., 1954
Mixed Calisthenics and Cross-country	L. A. Golding	Ph.D., 1958
	E. E. Phillips	Ph.D., 1960
Twenty-six weeks of Marine Underwater Demolition Training	J. W. Tuma	Ph.D., 1959
Ice Skating	G. E. Marcotte	M.S., 1960
Walking Uphill on a Portable Treadmill and Rowing	A. E. Domke	M.S., 1955
	S. R. Brown	M.S., 1957
Mixed Calisthenics, Jogging and Swimming	H. K. Campney	M.S., 1953
Underwater Scuba Swimming	P. S. Carhart	M.S., 1956
Use of a Health Walker	E. L. Herden	M.S., 1956
Badminton	L. F. Sterling	M.S., 1956
Mixed P.E. Activities	W. M. Kruzic	M.S., 1948
Mixed Calisthenics	L. R. Harrison	M.S., 1949
Calisthenics	H. P. Wells	M.S., 1950
Prescribed Exercises for Parts of the Body	M. Wolfson	M.S., 1951
Walking, Home Calisthenics and Golf*	T. K. Cureton*	

*Work published in *Res Quart,* 23:149-160, May 1952.

These studies have been summarized in a report given in 1951 by Cureton; in another in 1952 at Helsinki, Finland at the International Congress of Sports Medicine and Physiology; and again at the University of Illinois Colloquium in 1960.

Certain of these studies could be transferred to standard scores so that comparisons could be made (Table B-IV). The results show that marked improvements in the brachial pulse wave were made in the area under the wave, the systolic amplitude, the diastolic surge, and the work-to-rest ratio. These improvements paralleled improvements made in muscular endurance, run times, and various other fitness measurements.[75, 76, 77]

TABLE B-IV

COMPARATIVE IMPROVEMENTS IN CARDIOVASCULAR TESTS RESULTING FROM PROGRAMS WITH MIDDLE-AGED MEN*

(In Standard Scores)

Name	Type of Program	No. of Subjects	Area	BRACHIAL PULSE WAVE				Schneider Index	Five-Min Step Test	Barach Index
				Systolic Ampl	Diastolic Ampl	Diastolic Surge	Rest to Work Ratio			
Hopkins	Volleyball and calisthentics	16	17.88	17.88	9.31	19.5	-5.44	10.31		
Wolbers	Volleyball	9	2.67	4.33	3.22	-4.11	1.44	7.22	-22.67	
Harrison	Swimming	8	5.5					3.75	5.28	
Domke	Rowing machine	3	9.0	7.33	8.33	21.67		-3.0	13.33	3.67
Bryant	Handball	9	7.78	12.89	20.01	10.45	3.78	12.78	11.11	
Kristufek	Endurance training	1	25.0	15.0	20.0		40.0	12.0	18.0	13.0
Herden	Health-walker	2	20.5	15.5	25.0	28.5	20.0	16.0	19.5	16.5
Brodt	Weight lifting	6	7.17	1.0	9.17	21.15	4.83	12.5	7.17	
Campney	Physical activity	1	3.0	-2.0	-1.0	-39.0	0	15.0	-24.0	
Nakamura	Swimming	1	37.0	34.0	40.0	5.0	9.0	20.0	20.0	6.0
Wolfson	Prescribed exercise	9	2.11	11.33	1.0	24.44	.11	12.22		
Herkimer	Physical activity	12	13.5	14.17	16.83	8.58	7.83	6.67	8.8	

Note: Average SS improvement used for comparison.

*Various studies at the University of Illinois, completed under the supervision of Professor T. K. Cureton, are more completely described in the original theses or in Abstracts of Graduate Studies (edited by T. K. Cureton, 213 Huff Gymnasium, Urbana, Ill.)

Parallel Improvement of Systolic Amplitude of Heartograph with Electrocardiogram T-Wave, Pulse Rate, and Ballistocardiogram IJ Waves

Liverman's study with Cureton at Illinois shows the parallel improvement in the amplitude of the highest precordial T-wave of the ECG, the BCG (Arbeit Direct Body), and the quiet, sitting brachial pulse wave.[78] In the last 22 weeks of the 27-week experiment, there was a reduction in the sitting pulse rate. This reduction in pulse rate is paralleled by a reduction in the vigor of the HI and IJ complexes in the BCG. Both were undoubtedly related to reduced total peripheral resistance in the subjects. The same phenomenon has also been shown by Knowlton[79] in a similar experiment in our department. Liverman's subjects covered 3 miles per day, 5 days per week in running but had about 20 minutes of brisk calisthenics before running. Tests were made at the beginning of the program several times to check reliability (T_0), again 5 weeks after the running had begun (T_1), and again at the end of the program (T_3) (26-27 weeks) (Figs. B-46, B-47). The ages of the men ranged from 26 to 55 years. The mile run time improved as an average from 8.05 minutes to 6.22 minutes, and the all-out treadmill run time improved from 3.63 to 6.56 minutes, both of these over the last 22 weeks of the experiment. This was due to abstaining from testing the men until they had adjusted to the running. The Harvard Step Test reduced from 183 to 161 beats in the recovery count periods (1 to 1:30; 2 to 2:30; 3 to 3:30 minutes). There was marked reduction in peripheral resistance in the men, and they developed stronger and more responsive sympatho-adrenergic systems. In the latter stages of the training, with lower total peripheral resistance, there could have been smaller ejection force as indicated by the BCG results but slower pulse rates and stronger HGF waves.

Von Gadermann, Metzner, and Jungman[80] analyzed the change in shape of the pulse waves due to training, pointing to the increased systolic amplitude, the increased depth of the dicrotic notch, and the increased strength of the diastolic "rebound" wave; then they superimposed the trained waves over the untrained ones in the same subject (Fig. B-48).

Pulse Waves and Pathological Cardiovascular Condition

R. B. Willcutt[81] reported that out of forty-eight coronary patients, the cardiac output was decreased 40 percent in the resting state, which he attributed to enlarged hearts and prolonged circulatory time. Christensen,[82] years ago, found that the totally untrained subject usually has a fast pulse and a low stroke volume—vice versa for the fully trained person. He observed a significant increase in stroke volume as a result of training of athletes which he states was associated with some enlargement of the heart.

A good basic interpretative guide to the various deflections, notches,

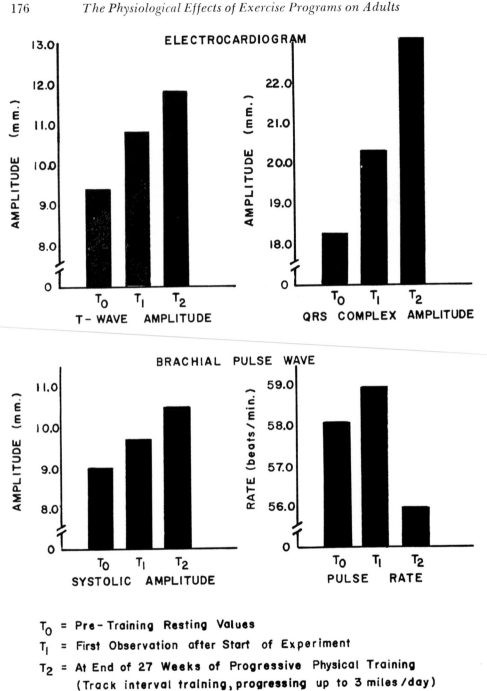

T$_0$ = Pre-Training Resting Values

T$_1$ = First Observation after Start of Experiment

T$_2$ = At End of 27 Weeks of Progressive Physical Training
(Track interval training, progressing up to 3 miles/day)

FIGURE B-46. Effect of progressive physical training upon the precordial T-waves and QRS complex of the electrocardiogram, and upon systolic amplitude of the brachial pulse wave and pulse rate. N = thirty middle-aged men. (Liverman and Cureton, 1965.)

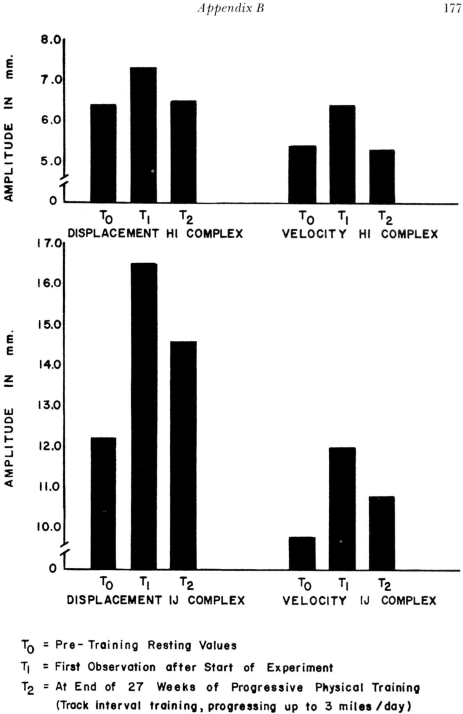

T_0 = Pre-Training Resting Values

T_1 = First Observation after Start of Experiment

T_2 = At End of 27 Weeks of Progressive Physical Training
(Track interval training, progressing up to 3 miles/day)

FIGURE B-47. Effect of progressive physical training upon the direct body ballistocardiogram. HI and IJ amplitudes. N = thirty middle-aged men. (Liverman and Cureton, 1965.)

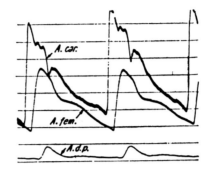

FIGURE B-48.   Pattern of trained brachial pulse wave. (von E. Gadermann, Metzner, and Jungman.)

and areas is Wiggers' *Circulatory Dynamics.*[83] Isaac Starr and F. G. Wood[84] have shown in a 20-year follow-up study of 211 business executives from the Philadelphia downtown area that, on the basis of the first BCG's taken, the men with low, flat, or rounded peaks (slow velocity and/or acceleration) were predominantly the ones to trigger into coronary attacks; whereas, the large, tall (high velocity and/or acceleration) waves were relatively immune in this same 20-year period.

Low, flat, and "sluggish" pulse waves are similar in meaning, indicating high TPR and "loafer's heart" characteristics. A high relationship exists between the BCG and heartographs if the comparisons are made in the same velocity and acceleration units on the same person at the same time. The intercorrelations of simple displacement pulse waves with velocity BCG's (Arbeit direct body BCG machine) were found to be 0.45 in our laboratory with this type of BCG correlating 0.80 with the ultralow frequency Ballisti-cor type waves. Simultaneous recording is needed to show this, comparing velocity with velocity, or acceleration with acceleration.

Wiggers[85] states that arterial resistance and venous inflow are the more important determiners of stroke output—not pulse rate. We agree, and thousands of observations have shown that high blood pressures and high TPR are most highly associated with "flattish," low amplitude waves. Since Wiggers has covered so well the basic interpretations, they are not repeated here.

Weissler, Harris, and White[86] reported that the left ventricular index (LVI) (0.395-.0016 HR for 110 males and 0.415-.0016 HR for females), measured from the beginning of the upstroke to the incisura, correlated 0.69 with the cardiac index. A longer LVI goes with slower heart rate. The LVI was highly reproducible. There is a decrease in LVI with (congestive) myocardial failure due to hypertensive heart disease or idiopathic myocardial failure corresponding to a decrease in stroke volume.

Karfman, Payne, and Travis Winsor[87] state, "The presence of arterial disease is, as a rule, easily detectable by observing the amplitude and morphology of the pulse waves. The abnormal waves usually exhibit a significant decrease in pulse amplitude, an insignificant or absent dicrotic notch, a prolonged crest time, a rounded or flattened peak, and a slow rate or rise of the anacrotic limb."

Cooper, Hill, and Edwards[88] state, "Previous experience with external pulse recording in this laboratory shows it to be capable of detecting partial as well as complete arterial obstruction. Some of the pulse changes in arteriosclerosis, such as a loss of the dicrotic notch or the presence of aberrant vibration, are not regularly present nor easily measured. True measurements can be defined numerically and may thus be used (1) rate of ascent of systole (or slope), (2) pulse amplitude (vertical deflections)."

Starr and Wood[89] made a follow-up study of business executives (22 to 85 years, 174 men and 37 women), using the ballistocardiogram (high frequency) method after lying for 15 minutes and being 2 hours away from a meal. After 20 years, sixty-five men and twenty-three women survived. The subjects with low IJ amplitude waves, proportional to the *force* of ejection of the blood from the heart developed more than 80 percent of the attacks; whereas, the subjects with the strong IJ deflections were, in this same period of time, relatively immune (Fig. B-49). Starr also reported that it made no difference which type of BCG was used as the high and low frequency deflections intercorrelated 0.91.

Five-channel Oscillograph Results, Relations to Brachial Pulse Wave

Using a Brecht-Boucke capacitance transducer strapped over the brachial artery and also an Infratron Pulse Signal Divider to filter the frequencies picked up by the transducer to give a palpatory record of the pulse contour, the signal voltage from the Infratron was amplified by an oscilloscope and differentiated first and second derivatives with the aid of a Heath Operational Amplifier. The records were graphed by a Grass Polygraph Recorder as all data were taken simultaneously. The pulse wave, the first derivative, the second derivative, the ballistocardiogram, and the electrocardiogram were recorded on channels 1, 2, 3, 4, 5, respectively. Banister and Cureton, Pollard and Abbott[90] reported data of the type shown in Figure B-53 comparing athletes, normals and heart-disease subjects. In the record illustrated, the brachial pulse wave is shown at the top; then the second and first derivatives, then the BCG, and finally the ECG. The dotted vertical lines show the peak acceleration, and peak velocity amplitudes, left to right. The first solid vertical line is erected through Q, the point where the electrical stimuli begin in the QRS complex. The first sign of heart muscular contraction is where the second vertical line crosses the horizontal base axis, and Q to this

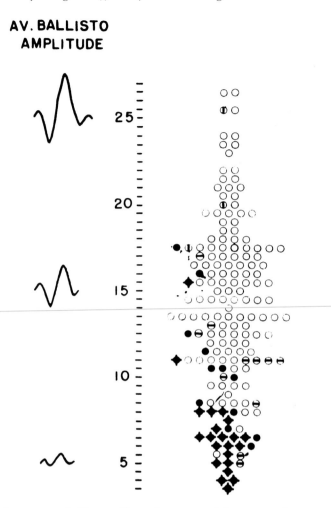

FIGURE B-49. Low energy ballistocardiograph waves and frequency of coronary attack. Black, round circles indicate attack but not death; squares indicate death on the attack. (Starr and Wood, 1961.)

point, measured horizontally in seconds (0.143), is the latent tension period (TP) when pressure builds up in the left ventricle. Ejection is timed with the third vertical line. The time known as ICP (isovolumic period) is between the last two lines. Several studies involving these intervals, some done with the method used by Raab (Blumberger's method, Fig. B-54), have been completed.

Cureton and Du Toit[91] reported the results of two relatively hard progressive training programs which were conducted by Banister and Liverman. Since their approach was not on the pre-ejection intervals but their data permitted the measurement of the intervals, Cureton and du Toit carried out the work. Banister's training program was composed of jogging and circuit training, involved climbing stairs for time, and lasted for 16 weeks. Liverman's program was composed of jogging, calisthenics, hard running, and bench stepping (repetitious bouts for 1, 2, 3, 4, and 5 min. on a 17-in. bench). Both programs caused a *shortening* of the TP interval which was the same interval measured by Raab. Raab's theory was that the interval should lengthen, and sometimes it does, provided the program is less severe as in moderate cycling and dancing.

In the Banister-Cureton-Abbott-Pollard study, the younger athletic men had the faster ejection strokes (vertically or in the time for the curve to rise from the base axis to the peak), and they also had much faster relaxation phases of the stroke. The athletic man has a longer diastolic filling time, especially in the postexercise period of recovery (5 minutes). Definite improvements in these waves were brought about by the progressive physical training. The "initial impulse" of the ventricular contraction, as indicated by Rushmer, Spencer, and Greiss[92] and others implies a stronger initial force (F) acting to eject the blood. Rushmer describes the impact of the heart muscle in the initial stage of contraction as it acts on the blood as a "hammer-like blow." The force (F) acts to propel the mass of blood into the aorta, to distend it, and to elicit its elastic recoil. The F is obviously the same to affect the IJ complex of the BCG (with slight suspension losses), and the "time to peak"in the heartograph is likewise affected. Figure B-32 shows the differences between trained subjects in the BCG; Figures B-33, B-43, and B-52 show variations obtained in the heartographs.

Raab[93] maintains that the ICP interval reflects sympathetic stimulation of the left ventricular musculature, and a greater ejection tension results. Sloniger was unable to show any correlation between the ICP or EML intervals, or TP, as related to all-out ergometer bicycle ride time. But Banister was able to show correlation 0.74 between the "rise to peak" time for the anacrotic slope of the brachial pulse wave. The pulse rate itself was poorly correlated (0.22). Nevertheless, these intervals in the cardiac cycle have been shown to be related to aging and to status of the autonomic nervous system at rest (i.e., to determine if an individual can relax when he should). Usually athletes with competition on their minds show considerable tension, but a workout relaxes them somewhat even though they may retain tension until their season is over.

Figure B-53, taken on a middle-aged businessman who complained of nervous tension due to losing a large sum of money in a sale of some apartment buildings, showed considerable pre-ejection interval tension before his workout; but, after the workout, there was a lengthening of the TP interval. He was tested at rest; then 2½ minutes after stepping up and down on a 17-inch bench for 2 minutes (center); and again about 40 minutes after his

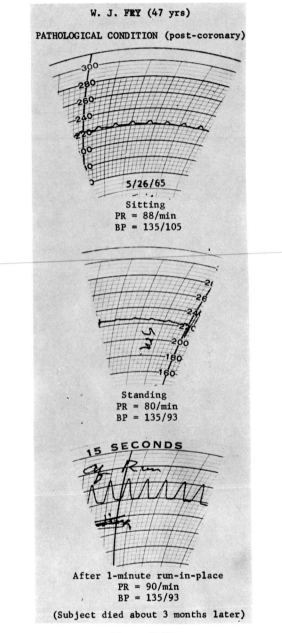

FIGURE B-50.

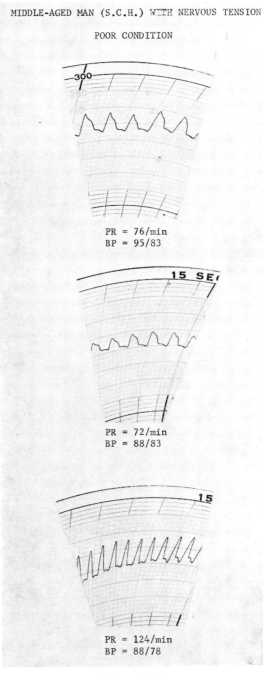

MIDDLE-AGED MAN (S.C.H.) WITH NERVOUS TENSION

POOR CONDITION

PR = 76/min
BP = 95/83

PR = 72/min
BP = 88/83

PR = 124/min
BP = 88/78

FIGURE B-51.

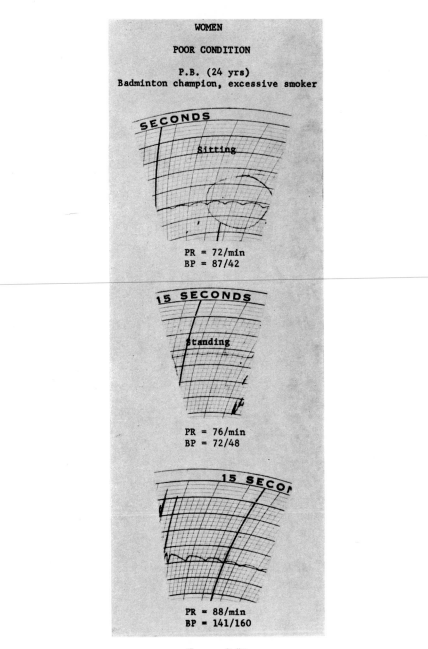

FIGURE B-52.

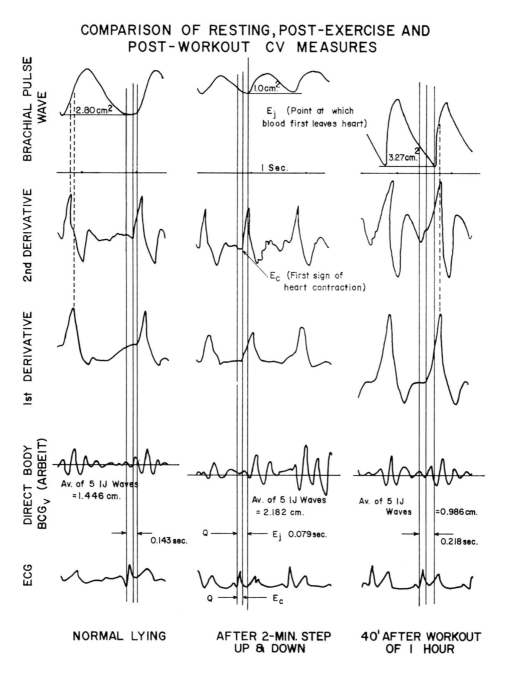

FIGURE B-53.

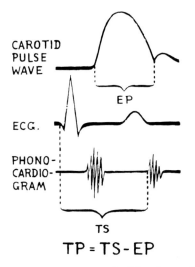

CAROTID
PULSE
WAVE

EP

ECG.

PHONO-
CARDIO-
GRAM

TS

TP = TS - EP

FIGURE B-54. Chronodynogram. Blumberger method for determining TP (Tension Period). (Used by Dr. Wilhelm Raab.)

workout (involving walking, jogging, and some calisthenics, covering about 2 miles). The TP interval, between the second and third vertical lines, was then wider between the lines indicating the relaxation. The exercise appeared to have a relaxing effect, and we know from correlative experiments that exercise of this type reduces the total peripheral resistance.

Harrison,[94] in discussing heart records of this type, states that this faster relaxation phase, characterized by the deep deceleration curve of the second derivative relaxation curve, is a most important indicator of youth and fitness in the heart muscle, and it is usually found to be just the opposite in coronary cases as our records show. Hyman[95] has, likewise, pointed out that the Q to first heart sound interval shortens in fitter men and is elongated in old age, in poor states of fitness, and in sickness.

Sloniger[96] and and Cundiff[97] have also studied the EML (Q to first heart sound) and the ICP (first heart sound to beginning of ejection) and have concluded that these pre-ejection intervals are not related to performance time on the ergometer bicycle; whereas, Weber demonstrated good correlations for the amplitude of the heartograph, maximal oxygen intake capacity, and terminal pulse rate. The ICP is most sensitive to stress, even more so than the oxygen debt, and evenly so with eosinophils. The more able the subjects, the more they can tolerate the stress of exertion by all of these indications. Weber[98] concluded that the systolic amplitude of the brachial pulse wave of the Cameron heartograph was the best to predict the all-out treadmill run time.

Rodbard[99] reported that the Q to first heart sound (EML) shortens in proportion to stroke output, the normal interval being 0.210, and shortens to 0.170 seconds in exercise. J. C. P. Williams and E. H. Wood[100] found, with the computer analysis of central aortic pulses in dogs, that the stroke volume was at a maximum when A-V delay was shortest (0.083 seconds).

References

1. Cureton, T. K.: *Physical Fitness Appraisal and Guidance.* St. Louis, Mosby, 1947 (pictures, definitions for quantitation and operational instructions and some normative tables).
2. Cameron Co.: *The Heartometer in the Field of Physical Education* (excerpts from work of T. K. Cureton). Chicago, Cameron Heartometer Co.
3. Uvnas, B.: Sympathetic vasodilator outflow. *Physiol Rev, 34*:608-618, July 1954.
4. Hartman, F. A.; Evans, J. I., and Walker, H. G.: Control of the capillaries of skeletal muscle. *Amer J Physiol, 90*:668+, Nov. 1929.
5. Cureton, T. K.: *Physical Fitness of Champion Athletes.* Urbana, U. of Ill., 1951.
6. Cureton, T. K.: Sympathetic versus vagus influence upon the contractile vigor of the heart. *Res Quart, 32*:553-557, Dec. 1961.
7-9. Cureton, T. K.: Physical training produces important changes, psychological and physiological. In Karvonen, M. J. (Ed.): *International Symposium of Sports-Medicine and Physiology,* XVth Olympiad, Helsinki, 1953, pp. 46-63. Also summary of research, Anatomical, physiological and psychological changes induced by exercise programs (exercises, sports, games) in adults. In *Exercise and Fitness,* U. of Ill. Colloquium, 1960. Chicago, Athletic Institute.
10. Cureton, T. K., and Du Toit, S.: Effect of progressive physical training on the latent period of electrical stimulation of the left ventricle of the human heart. *Proc College Phys Educ Ass,* 69th Annual Meeting at Philadelphia, 1965, pp. 121-122.
11. Sloniger, E. L.: The Relationship of Stress Indicators to Pre-ejection Cardiac Intervals. Ph.D. Thesis, U. of Ill., 1966.
12. Cundiff, David: Training Changes in the Sympatho-Adrenal System Determined by Cardiac Cycle Hemodynamics, O_2 Intake and Eosinopenia. Ph.D. Thesis, U. of Ill., 1966.
13. Weber, H.: A Quantitative Study of Eosinopenia and Other Stress Indices. Ph.D. Thesis, U. of Ill., 1965.
14. Wolkowitz, W., and Fich, S.: A nonuniform hybrid model of the aorta. *Trans N Y Acad Sci (Ser. II), 29*:316-331, Jan. 1967.
15. Skouby, A. P.: The morphology of the pulse curve of the aorta. Copenhagen, Laboratory of Theoretical Gymnastics, U. of Copenhagen. *Acta Physiol Scand, 10*: 374-380, 1945.
16. Remington, J. W., and Hamilton, W. F.: The construction of a theoretical cardiac ejection curve from the contour of the aortic pressure pulse. *Amer J Physiol, 144*:546-556, Sept. 1945.
17. Rushmer, R. F.: Pressure-circumference relations in the aorta. *Amer J Physiol, 183*:545, 1955.
18. Wiggers, C. J.: *The Pressure Pulses in the Cardiovascular System.* London and New York, Longmans, Green and Co., 1928.
19. Attinger, E. O. (Ed.): *Pulsatile Blood Flow.* New York, McGraw, 1964.

20. McDonald, D. A.: *Blood Flow in Arteries.* Monograph of the Physiol Soc, (No. 7). London, Edward Arnold, 1960.

21. Henderson, Y.: The volume curve of the ventricles of the mammalian heart and the significance of the curve in respect to the mechanics of the heart-beat and the filling of the ventricles. *Amer J Physiol, 16*:325-367, July 1906.

22. Frank, O.: Grundform des Arterialen Pulses. *Z Biol, 37*:483, 1809; and *46*:441, 1905.

23. Wiggers, *op. cit.*

24. Wiggers, C. J.: *Circulatory Dynamics.* New York, Grune, 1952.

25. Wiggers, *Ibid.*

26. Hamilton, W. F.: The patterns of the arterial pressure pulse. *Amer J Physiol, 141*:235, March 1944; and with Remington, J. W., and Dow, P.: Some difficulties in the prediction of the stroke volume from the pulse wave velocity. *Amer J Physiol, 144*:536-545, Sept. 1945.

27. Brown, E. W., Jr.; Bunnell, I. L., and Green, D. G.: Effects of hemodynamic changes on the shape of the arterial pressure pulse curve. *Amer J Physiol, 179,* Dec. 1954.

28. Skouby, A. P.: The patterns of the arterial pressure pulse. *Amer J Physiol* and; *Acta Physiol Scand, 10*:374-380, 1943.

29. Cureton, T. K.: The nature of cardiovascular condition in normal humans. Parts I, II and III. *J Phys Ment Rehab, 11*:186-196, Nov.-Dec. 1957; *12*:8-12, Jan.-Feb. 1958; *12*:41-49, Jan.-Feb. 1958.

30. Cureton, T. K., and Massey, B. H.: Brachial peripheral pulse waves related to altitude tolerance and endurance. *Amer J Physiol, 159,* Dec. 1949.

31. Cureton, T. K.: *Physical Fitness of Champion Athletes.* Urbana, U. of Ill., 1951, p. 221. (The ECG decrement wave in the decompression chamber is shown.)

32. Dontas, A. S.: Comparison of simultaneously recorded intra-arterial and extra-arterial pressure pulse in man. *Amer Heart J, 59*:576, 1960, *61*:676-683, May 1961.

33. Dontas, A. S.: Arterial and pressure pulse contours in the young human subject. *Amer Heart J, 61*:676-683, May 1961.

34. Rushmer, R. F., and Crystal, D. K.: Changes in the configuration of the ventricular chambers during the cardiac cycle. *Circ Res, 1*:162-170, 1953.

35. Kroeker, E. J., and Wood, E. H.: Comparison of simultaneously recorded central and peripheral pressure pulses during rest and exercise and tilted position in man. *Circ Res, 3*:623+, 1955.

36. Heyman, F.: Comparison of intra-arterially and extra-arterially recorded pulse waves in man and dog. *Acta Med Scand, 157*:503, 1957.

37. Kroeker and Wood, *op. cit.*

38. Cureton, T. K.: *The Heartometer in the Field of Physical Education.* Chicago, Cameron Heartometer Corporation, 1954.

39. Cureton, T. K.: What the heartometer reveals that is of interest to physical education and physical fitness directors. *Phys Educ Today, 7* (No. 1):10-14, March 1960.

40. Ibid.: (in French) *Revue de L'Education Physique* (Liege, Belgium), *1*:796-1003, Sept. 1961; *190*:1-12, 1959.

41. Cureton, T. K., and Massey, B. H.: Brachial peripheral pulse waves related to altitude tolerance and endurance. *Amer J Physiol, 159*:566, Dec. 1949.

42. Massey, B. H.: Changes in the Cameron Heartometer and Johnson Oscillometer

Pulse Wave Tracings with Progressive Loads of Work. Ph.D. Thesis, Physical Education, U. of Ill., 1950.

43. STRYDOM, N. P.: Changes in Cardiac Output with Progressive Work. Ph. D. Thesis, Physical Education, U. of ill., 1950.

44. FOX, E. F.: A comparison of the Cameron Heartometer with the Johnson Oscillometer. M.S. Thesis, Physical Education, U. of Ill., 1950.

45. MICHAEL, E. D.: Relationships Between the Heartometer and the Acetylene Method of Measuring Circulatory Fitness. M.S. Thesis, Physical Education, U. of Ill., 1949.

46. LANDOWNE, M.; BRANDFONBRENNER, M., and SHOCK, N. W.: The relationship of age to certain measures of performance of the heart and circulation. *Circulation, 12*:567-576, Oct. 1955.

47. KARVONEN, M., and BARRY, ALAN J.: *Physical Activity and the Heart.* Springfield, Ill., Thomas, 1967, p. 405.

48. MICHAEL, E. D., and CURETON, T. K.: Effects of physical training on cardiac output at ground level and at 15,000 feet simulated altitude. *Res Quart, 24*:446-452, Dec. 1953.

49. WANG, Y.; MARSHALL, R. J., and SHEPHERD, J. T.: The effect of changes in posture and graded exercise on stroke volume in man. *J Clin Invest, 39*:1051-61, July 1960.

50. WREN, E. A.: The Effects of Interference Upon the Brachial Pulse Wave in Various Posture Positions with and without Venous Impedance, M.S. Thesis, Physical Education, U. of Ill., 1962.

51. CURETON, T. K.: The nature of cardiovascular condition in normal humans, Part II. *J Phys Ment Rehab, 12*:8-12, 1958.

52. MASSEY, B. H.; HUSMAN, B. H., and KEHOE, C. L.: The effect of posture on brachial sphygmograms as an indicator of cardiovascular condition. *Res Quart, 24*:194-204, May 1953.

53. WARNER, H. R., *et al.*: Quantitation of beat-to-beat changes in stroke volume from aortic pulse contour in man. *J Appl Physiol, 5*:495-507, March 1953.

54. HUGGINS, R. A., and SMITH, E. L.: Validity of the pulse contour method for determining cardiac output. *Fed Proc, 11*:767-773, Sept. 1952.

55. SWAN, H. J. C., *et al.*: Quantitation of stroke volume changes in man from peripheral arterial pressure pulses. *Amer J Physiol, 171*, Dec. 1952.

56. JONES, W. B.; HEFNER, L. L.; BANCROFT, W. H., and CHIP, W.: *Amer Heart Ass Mono* (Abstract I), 1960, p. 114.

57. SPENCER, M. P.; JOHNSON, F. R., and DENISON, A. B.: *Circ Res, 6*:491-500, 1958.

58. WILLIAMS, J. C. P., and WOOD, E. H.: Changes in stroke volume determined by real time analysis of aortic pulse contour during computer controlled variation of A-V stimulus interval. *Fed Proc* (Abstract No. 99), *25*:206, March-April 1966.

59. BROWN, E. W., JR.; BUNNELL, I. L., and GREENE, D. G.: Effects of hemodynamic changes on the shape of the arterial pressure pulse curve. *Amer J Physiol, 179,* Dec. 1954.

60. KENDRICK, J. E.: Aortic pressure pulses produced by controlled flow input. *Psysiologist, 9*:217, August 1966.

61. FREIS, E. D.; LUCKSINGER, P. C.; SNELL, R. E., and HEATH, W. C.: Changes in the carotid pulse wave with age and hypertension. *Amer Heart J, 71*:757, June 1966; and *Circulation, 34*:423, Sept. 1966.

62. CURETON, T. K.: The nature of cardiovascular fitness and its protection by exer-

cise-fitness programs. *J Phys Educ (YMCA), 61*:30-34, Nov.-Dec. 1963; also in *Sportarzt (Cologne), 7*:230-236, 1962.

63. CURETON, T. K., and STERLING, L. F.: Factor analyses of cardiovascular test variables. *J Sport Med, 4* (No. 1):1-24, March 1964.

64. CURETON, T. K.: Comparison of various factor analyses of cardiovascular-respiratory test variables. *Res Quart, 37*:317-325, Dec. 1966.

65. STARR, I., and OGAWA, S.: On the aging of the heart, etc. *Amer J Med Sci, 549* (No. 4), Oct. 1960; *243*:309, 1962.

66. RUSHMER, R. F.: Initial ventricular impulse. *Circ Res, 24*:268, 1964.

67. BANISTER, E.; CURETON, T. K.; ABBOTT, B. C., and POLLARD, J. W. (M.D.): *J Sport Med 6*:92-99, June 1966.

68. CURETON, T. K.: *Physical Fitness of Champion Athletes.* Urbana, U. of Ill., 1951, pp. 230-249.

69. CURETON, T. K.: *Physical Fitness Appraisal and Guidance.* St. Louis, Mosby, 1947, pp. 232-280.

70. JOKL, E., and WELLS, J. B.: Exercise training and cardiac force. In RAAB, W. (Ed).: *Prevention of Ischemic Heart Disease.* Springfield, Thomas, 1966, pp. 135-146.

71. GLICK, GERALD, and BRAUNWALD, EUGENE: Relative roles of the sympathetic and parasympathetic nervous systems in reflex control of the heart rate. *Circ Res, 16*:363-375, April 1965.

72. HALL, VICTOR E.: The relation of heart rate to exercise fitness: an attempt at physiological interpretation of the bradycardia of training. *Pediatrics,* Part II, Oct. 1963, pp. 723-729.

73. CURETON, T. K.: Sympathetic versus vagus influence upon the contractile vigor of the heart. *Res Quart, 32*:553-557, Dec. 1961.

74. KRISTUFEK, C. J.: The Effect of Endurance Training on an Adult Subject, M.S. Thesis, Physical Education, U. of Ill., 1951.

75. CURETON, T. K.: Review of research to determine cardiovascular condition, 1941-50. Washington, *Proc AAHPER* (56th Annual Convention Report, Detroit), 1951, pp. 167-177.

76. CURETON, T. K.: Physical training produces important changes, psychological and physiological. In KARVONEN, M. (Ed.): *International Symposium of Sports-Medicine and Physiology.* Helsinki, 1953.

77. CURETON, T. K.: *Exercise and Fitness,* U. of Ill. Colloquium. Athletic Institute, U. of Ill., 1960, pp. 152-182.

78. LIVERMAN, R. D.: Effects of Vigorous Physical Training on Simultaneous Cardiovascular Records. Ph.D. Thesis, Physical Education, U. of Ill., 1965.

79. KNOWLTON, R. G.: A Ballistocardiographic Investigation of Cardiac Response to Physical Training with a Select Group of Adult Males. Ph.D. Thesis, Physical Education, U. of Ill., 1961.

80. VON E. GADERMANN; METZNER, A., and JUNGMAN, H.: Training suthekte am Arterienpuls. *Der Sportarzt,* Sept. 1961, pp. 60-62.

81. WILLCUTT, R. B.: Resting cardiac output determinations in the wounded heart. *J AOA, 65*:169/93 to 180/104.

82. CHRISTENSEN, E.: Beitrage zur Physiologie Schwerer Koeperlicher Arbeit. *Arbeitsphysiologie, 4*:470-502, 1931.

83. WIGGERS, C. J.: The clinical importance of arterial pulse tracings. New York, *Circulatory Dynamics.* Grune, 1952, pp. 18-26, 40-50, 53-101.

84. STARR, ISAAC, and WOOD, F. G.: Twenty-year studies with the ballistocardiograph. *Circulation, 23*:714-732, May 1961.

85. WIGGERS, C. J.: *Circulatory Dynamics.* New York, Grune, 1952, p. 38.

86. WEISSLER, A. M.; HARRIS, L. C., and WHITE, G. D.: Left ventricular ejection time index in man. *J Appl. Physiol, 18*:919-923, 1963.

87. KARFMAN, H. L.; PAYNE, J. H., and WINSOR, TRAVIS: A practical systematic laboratory approach to the study of the peripheral circulation. *Amer Heart J, 53*:306-318, August 1960.

88. COOPER, D.; HILL, L. T. JR., and EDWARDS, E. A.: Detection of early atherosclerosis by external pulse recording. *JAMA, 199*:109-114, Feb. 13, 1967.

89. STARR, I., and WOOD, F. G.: Twenty-year studies with the ballistocardiogram. *Circulation, 23*:714-732.

90. BANISTER, E. W.; CURETON, T. K.; ABBOTT, B. C., and POLLARD, J. W.: A comparative study of the brachial pulse wave and its time derivatives among athletic, normal and pathological subjects. *J Sport Med, 6*:92-99, June 1966.

91. CURETON, T. K., and DU TOIT, S. F.: Effect of progressive physical training on the latent period of electrical stimulation of the left ventricle of the human heart. *Proc College Phys Educ Ass,* 1965, pp. 121-122.

92. RUSHMER, R. F.: Initial ventricular impulse, a potential key to cardiac evaluation, *Circulation, 29*:253-282, Feb. 1964.

93. RAAB, W.: *Prevention of Ischemic Heart Disease.* Springfield, Thomas, 1966, pp. 121-134.

94. HARRISON, T. R., et. al.: The relation of age to the duration of contraction, ejection and relaxation of the normal heart. *Amer Heart J, 67*:189-199, Feb. 1964.

95. HYMAN, A. S.: The Q to first heart sound interval in athletes at rest and after exercise. *J Sport Med, 4*:199-203, Dec. 1964.

96. SLONIGER, E. L.: The Relationship of Stress Indicators to Pre-Ejection Cardiac Intervals. Ph.D. Thesis, Physical Education, U. of Ill., 1966.

97. CUNDIFF, D.: Training Changes in the Sympatho-adrenal System Determined by Cardiac Cycle Hemodynamics, O_2 Intake and Eosinopenia. Ph.D. Thesis, Physical Education, U. of Ill., 1967.

98. WEBER, H.: A Quantitative Study of Eosinopenia and Other Stress Indices. Ph.D. Thesis, Physical Education, U. of Ill., 1966.

99. RODBARD, S.: Timing of arterial sounds: An index of stroke output. Part II. *Fed Proc* (Abstract No. 98), *25*:205, March-April 1966.

100. WILLIAMS, JOHN C. P., and WOOD, E. H.: Changes in stroke volume by real time analysis of aortic pulse contour during computer controlled variation and stimulus interval. Part I. *Fed Proc.* (Abstract No. 99), *25*:206, March-April 1966.

APPENDIX C

OXYGEN INTAKE, DEFICIT (DEBT), AND ANOXIA PHOTOMETER TESTS

Cardiac Reserve

The very strong relationship between oxygen intake and endurance performance has been known since 1925, when the works of R. M. Sargent and A. V. Hill, biophysicists, brought this into scientific focus. Holding a faster pace for several minutes was shown to be primarily related to the oxygen intake capacity (aerobic). In a drive for the finish, the oxygen reserves were also called upon, at the expense of what was called "oxygen debt." The energy cost was computed as the total oxygen, adding the aerobic (intake) and anaerobic (debt) oxygen supplies together. Hill coined the term *oxygen requirement,* which was computed by dividing the total oxygen by the time of the effort. Great endurance was shown to be dependent upon the total oxygen supply, mainly the rate at which the body could use this oxygen when it was needed in a maximal type of performance. Physiologists showed that the amount of circulation and the "drinking up" of the oxygen by the tissues at work caused the absorption of oxygen from the lungs into the blood, and from the blood into the working cells of the body. The gross amount of the circulation was shown to be quite proportional to gross (aerobic) oxygen intake (not the debt). If a person worked harder than his aerobic oxygen supply would sustain, then an oxygen debt would develop. Margaria and Dill have explained that oxygen is used after the work to oxidize the fatigue products (metabolites), and oxygen must be returned to the hemoglobin of the blood and the myoglobin of the muscles, from which it was depleted.

Chesky[1] was one of the first to point out the significance of using oxygen intake during exercise as a quantitative means of estimating "cardiac reserve." Oxygen intake and debt work began as an assessment of work-cost earlier but came to be related to circulation through the work of Henderson.[2] As early as 1924, techniques had been devised to measure oxygen and oxygen debt during exercise. The first two groups to do this work and relate findings to endurance and heart output were, after Henderson, the Scandinavians Collett and Liljestrand.[3] The work was continued at the Harvard Fatigue Laboratory by Bock, Dill, and Talbott.[4] These all used ethyl iodide gas in

1928, and Bock, Dill and Talbott stated that the method was first used by Christensen, Douglas, and Haldane.

The ethyl iodide method gave way to the use of acetylene gas because of its more stable affinity with blood. Grollman[5, 6] developed its use between 1929 and 1932. The acetylene method was a cumbersome method but was effectively used by McMichael[7] and by Asmussen and Nielsen.[8] This method was validated against the Fick method by direct catheterization by Chapman[9] and was found to be quite consistent but gave values lower than the catheterization values. Brown demonstrated a moderate significant relationship between the ballistocardiographic cardiac output with Starr's method and oxygen intake.[10] Oxygen intake and the associated gross calculated circulation is not specifically a measure of coronary circulation.

The Cameron heartograph was validated in the University of Illinois Laboratory by Michael and by Cureton using the Grollman method for stroke volume.[11, 12] The amplitude and area correlated 0.91 and 0.88 with stroke volume, respectively. Cureton estimated that 38 cc per beat should be added as a constant correction in order that the Grollman or heartograph values should approximate the catheterization values.

Simonsen and Enzer[13] related cardiac output and oxygen intake capacity to evaluating the status of heart-disease subjects, stating that 1 liter per minute of oxygen (aerobic) was found to be the critical lower level of normality. The average is about 2.0 liters per minute in a maximal (single bag) test for normal middle-aged men. Simonsen also stated that any values below 1.0 are suggestive in a normal individual. In very debilitated cardiac patients who cannot step up and down on a bench, the values are not much above the resting levels. Hollman and Knipping[14] accept 2 liters per minute as the lower limit of normality as tested for oxygen intake on the Knipping apparatus. Balke and Clark[15] prefer to use a progressive series of trials, progressively increasing the slope of the treadmill 1 percent at 3.4 mi/hr for each working minute until the work is done. The evaluation is in cc per minute per kg: above 50 is excellent; above 45, very good; above 38, good; above 34, fair; and below 30, poor. On the low end of Balke's scale are hospitalized patients with chronic pulmonary disease, and at the upper end are athletes trained for great endurance performances. Further testing of coronary patients at Balke's laboratory at the Civil AA Research Center, Oklahoma City, has shown that coronary patients can do this test on a treadmill if they are carefully warmed up and progressively adjusted to the work.

Working capacity, as measured by maximal oxygen intake capacity, has been championed not only by Balke but even earlier by Astrand,[16] who sees the more critical aspect of physical fitness in this measure. He made comparisons between boys and girls, men and women, in an extensive series of tests.[17] The important point is that patients with heart and pulmonary

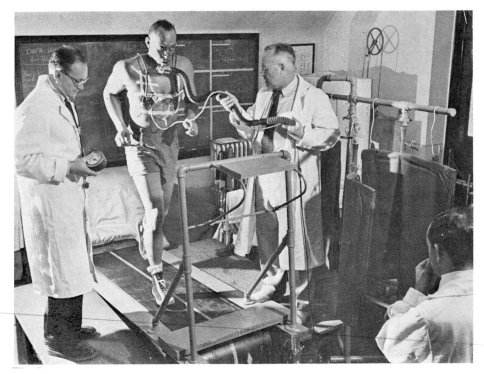

FIGURE C-1. Jesse Owens, 40 years of age, is tested on the treadmill at the University of Illinois laboratory.

disease (but not heart valvular disease) have much less working capacity and develop higher levels of oxygen deficiency and oxygen debt, the latter also shown by anoxia photometer techniques (Fig. C-1).

Methods for Testing All-out Capacity

The maximal oxygen intake under hard work is a prized measure. After a good warm-up, the subject runs on the treadmill (or rides the work bicycle) to virtual exhaustion. By varying only one variable, the length of the run (the endurance) and also the maximal circulatory capacity (oxygen intake capacity) are tested at the same time. For the purposes of physical education and athletics, this is the best type of test. It has certain limitations but conforms most closely to what a person would do in an actual race to see how far he could run in a given time.

Such a test was standardized at the Physical Fitness Research Laboratory in 1945[18] (Figs. C-2 and C-3). After much trial and error using various kinds of subjects, a test was set for 5, 7, or 10 mph, 8.6 percent grade. Women, children, and very old men were run on the first; normal young men and athletic women on the second; and athletes on the third. It it quite usual that a progression be used to go through the first, then the second, and then

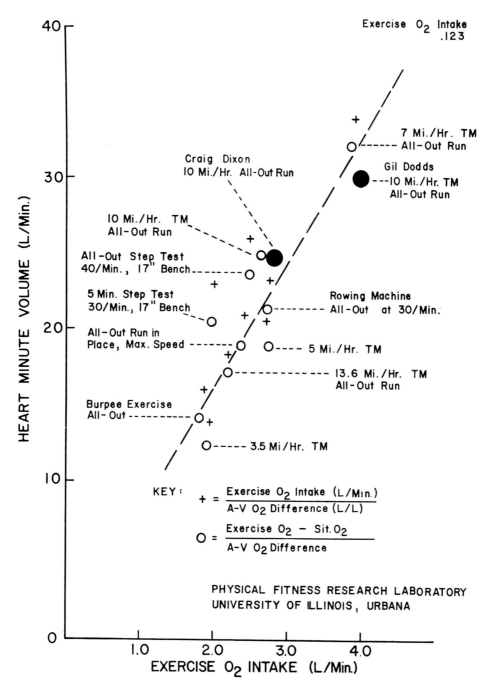

FIGURE C-2. Heart minute volume proportional to oxygen intake.

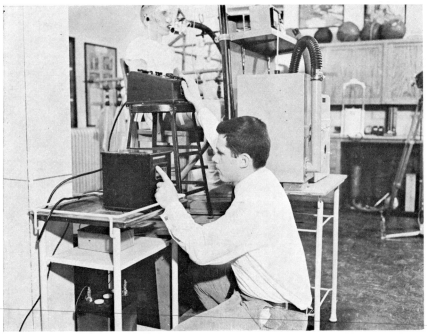

Figure C-3. Laboratory test of the blood. Using the anoxia photometer method for blood oxygen. The anoxia photometer is zeroed-in at 98 per cent O_2 saturation, to which the technician is pointing, while subject is seated; then the subject does the indicated exercise and the galvanometer indicator is carefully watched to note oxygen depletion. Physical Fitness Research Laboratory, U. of Ill.

Figure C-4. Blood ph is tested after hard exercise using the Beckman ph meter.

the third, depending upon the adjustment and the desire of the subjects. Blood pressures are taken before and 1.0 to 1.25 minutes after the all-out run, and sometimes the heartograph is also taken before and after the run. Terminal pulse rate is taken as soon as possible (within 10 sec) for a period of 15 seconds, and this is multiplied by four. Montoye,[19] using data loaned by D. B. Dill, found a correlation of 0.66 with the blood lactate measured just after the run (3 min after). Cureton made equations to predict the time of the 10 mph, 8.6 percent grade run from oxygen intake and rate of oxygen debt. It was shown that the top athletes ran all-out with less rate of net oxygen debt than the novices, and the athletes had much higher relative oxygen intake.

At first the test was given with one large Douglas bag to contain the expired gas during the run, from which the oxygen intake was computed after the gas was analyzed; other bags were used for the recovery. After a few years of using the *single bag oxygen intake test,* the single bag was replaced by a series of Douglas bags so that one could be used for each minute of run, or each half-minute[20, 21] (Fig. C-7). This gave higher peak values.

This work was the first to use multiple regression equations to predict the time of the run. The method also yielded causal analysis results by the beta weight (Doolittle) system, following the analytical statistical work on causes by Sewell Wright.[22]

The All-out Step Test

For use at *high gear,* after several months of preliminary work in a gradual build-up, the all-out step test is used with very fit subjects to determine their working capacity. It has been shown that this test correlates well with maximal oxygen intake capacity, used by many physiologists and sportsdoctors (Fig. C-8). It should not be attempted by beginners. It is scored in terms of seconds or minutes that a subject can keep going at 36 to 40 steps per minute. It corresponds to a hard treadmill run test, 10 mph at 8.6 percent grade. It should never be taken alone by anyone, and usually requires good warm-up and a physiologist or doctor to be present, not only as a safety precaution but also to take blood pressures and pulse rates before and after the event.

Substitute or Alternate Methods of Testing

Cureton[23] used 30 steps per minute for normal subjects in a substitute step test and 36 to 40 steps per minute in his work with former athletic champions after matching the treadmill oxygen intake with the oxygen intake in various rates of stepping. With male subjects the best substitute test for the 10-mph test on the treadmill was the test employing 36 to 40 steps per minute on the chair or 17-inch bench. This test is very satisfactory with athletic men. Only an occasional highly trained woman can do this test satisfactorily, but women can do the test at 30 steps per minute on a 17-inch chair or bench and the 7-mph treadmill run—as can all normal subjects (Figs. 4, 5, 6, and 7). Kasch[24] has reported a similar step test substitute for all-out treadmill running. Swedish workers have preferred the ergometer-bicycle-type test, and the German workers a manual "crank" type. There are marked differences between the results.

Cureton[25] also used the postexercise blood pressures taken just 1 minute after the cessation of the stepping or after the treadmill running as important tests to indicate circulatory-respiratory adjustment. A test using this data has not been fully scaled as yet, but it is viewed favorably in the developmental stages. To use this, the quiet sitting blood pressures are noted at a time when the subject is normal (not just before an all-out test). At a later time, usually the next day, the all-out run or step test is given. The terminal rate is taken for 15 seconds immediately after the run, and the blood pressures are taken immediately after this at 60 to 90 seconds. If the subject runs or steps with the cuff on, this time schedule can be met. We believe this to be an important test to indicate the adjustment which a subject could make to an all-out effort. If the subject fails to go as long as 2 minutes, the test should be repeated at a slightly slower pace.

Certain supplementary observations can, of course, be made. Cotton and Dill[26] point out that pulse rate *in moderate work,* just at the end of the run, is proportional to the work done—but by 20 seconds after the run, the pulse rate and the blood pressures have dropped considerably. Several studies support this simple postexercise pulse rate (within 10 sec at the cessation of the work). In our laboratory such "terminal" pulse rates have correlated as high as 0.68 with all-out treadmill run time.

Morehouse and Tuttle[27] also point out this same fact. By using an electrocardiotachometer, they have shown that terminal pulse rate at the end of a hard exercise is quite reliable—more so than at the end of easy exercise. They also have shown that the rate of the first few beats is directly related to the intensity of the exercise, and the recovery time is not related to the initial quiet pulse rate but is related to the intensity of the pulse rate. But after the pulse rate gets as high as 160 beats per minute or higher, the test has lower validity.

A method is now being studied which is based upon earlier work done with the heartometer brachial pulse waves. It was shown by Michael and by Michael and Cureton that the systolic amplitude and the area of the waves are highly related to the Grollman stroke volume. At pulse rates over 100, the heartometer pulse waves lose their characteristic area, but the work done and the oxygen intake of the subject during progressive levels of work are quite proportional to the *amplitude* of the bachial pulse waves.[28]

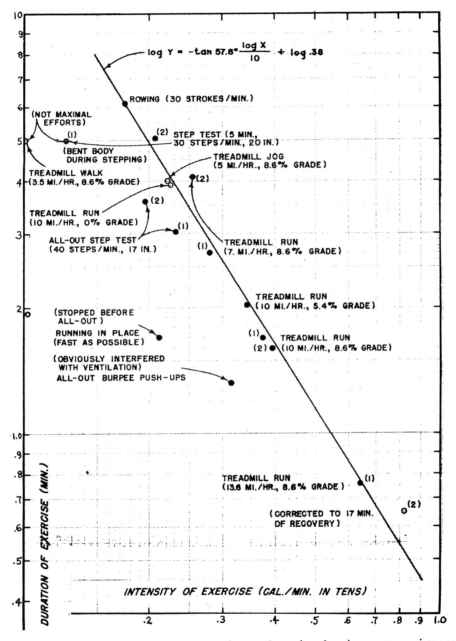

FIGURE C-5. Logarithmic plotting gives relative net intensity of various test exercises used in the laboratory.

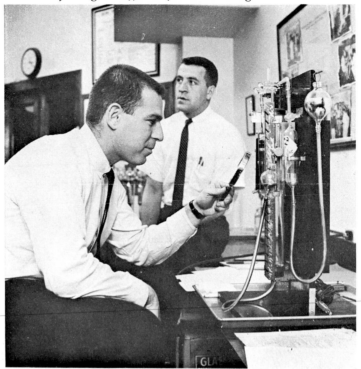

FIGURE C-6.   The Haldane gas analysis in the Physical Fitness Research Laboratory, U. of Ill.

FIGURE C-7.   Serial polyethylene bags used in the laboratory at the University of Illinois.

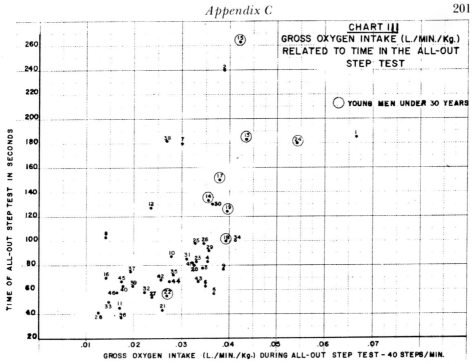

FIGURE C-8. The relationship of the all-out step test to maximal gross oxygen intake, highly correlated with circulatory capacity in hard work.

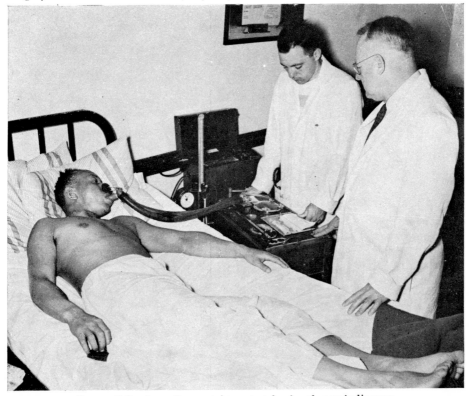

FIGURE C-9. Jesse Owens takes a test for basal metabolic rate.

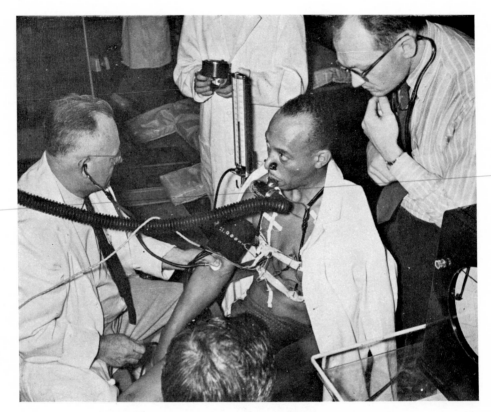

FIGURE C-10.   Jesse Owens takes quiet sitting O_2 intake test.

TABLE C-I

MEAN MAXIMUM VALUES

(From Astrand: *Experimental Studies of Physical Working Capacity in Relation to Sex and Age.* Copenhagen, Munksgaard, 1952.)

Age	MALES (N = 115) No.	Max. O_2 Intake ml/min/kg	Maximum Heart Rate	FEMALES (N = 112) No.	Max. O_2 Intake ml/min/kg	Maximum Heart Rate
4	4	48.2	201	2	44.7	195
5	3	52.9	205	3	50.4	208
6	3	46.2	206	2	47.2	207
7	2	58.7	203	3	56.0	209
8	3	56.0	218	4	52.3	205
9	7	56.8	206	7	56.4	215
10	6	55.1	215	6	51.8	206
11	7	54.9	207	7	52.9	210
12	9	56.4	196	6	51.0	207
13	10	56.5	213	7	48.7	208
14	5	59.2	204	5	47.7	202
15	5	59.7	202	6	44.7	202
16	3	59.0	199	8	47.0	207
17	3	58.2	201	2	47.9	201
18	3	55.6	205			
20	1			5	48.4	193
21	2			14	48.7	198
22 (3)	5	58.9	190	11	46.5	201
23 (2)				8	49.7	201
24	10	60.4	192	6	47.8	196
25	4	58.5	201			
26	3	58.8	200			
27	1					
28	5	58.5	192			
29	2	51.2	196			
30	4	58.3	188			
31	1					
32	2	57.4	198			
33	2					
Astrand Mean		56.5	201		49.5	204
Range		43.2—67.4	171—237		42.4—59.6	176—225
Cassels and Morse* Mean	9—17	47.8	195			
Robinson** Mean	10—17	50.7				

* Cassels, D. E., and Morse, M.: *Cardiopulmonary Data for Children and Young Adults.* Springfield, Thomas, 1962.

**Robinson, Sid (reported by Casseal): *Arbeitsphysiologie, 10*:251, 1938.

Note: Data tabulated for San Diego State College Exercise Laboratory by Dr. Fred W. Kasch, Ed.D., June 1962.

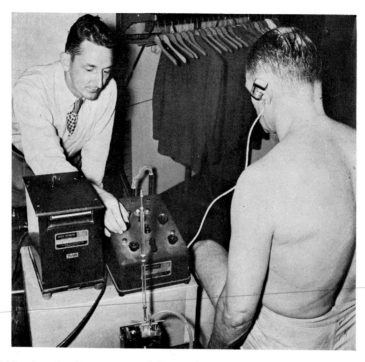

FIGURE C-11.   Anoxia photometer on left ear, showing direct reading galvanometer at left and control panel in middle.

The area breaks down as a valid measure if the pulse rate exceeds 100, but amplitude retains its validity (Figs. C-8 and C-9).

Table C-1 shows values for maximal O_2 (aerobic) intake as collected by Kasch from various studies. Unfortunately, there is a lack of standardization of equipment and atmospheric conditions; also there are differences due to constitutional body type, for which weight does not entirely correct. Relative fitness can be exactly determined only by following the same subject over the years of aging with the same equipment (valve, hose, rate of work, slope or resistance, etc.). Dill[29] has reported an interesting study to show marked deterioration over a 30-year period for several top-class endurance runners.

Predictions of short efforts, up to 1 to 6 minutes, involve oxygen debt as a factor, but Ribisl[30] has obtained high correlation ($R = 0.861$) between the maximal aerobic intake and 2-mile run time. Long distance run time is, in itself, a good substitute cardiovascular test (600 yd. or more) shown to correlate 0.70 and above with maximal oxygen intake.

An approximate proportional measure may be obtained during work by the use of the anoxia photometer method. It is necessary to "zero" the method in before the exertion test (Figs. C-11, C-12). If the arterial blood

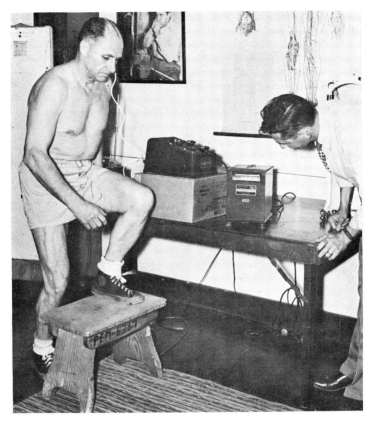

FIGURE C-12. Harvard Step Test shows no oxygen depletion for highly trained subject, Harold Osborn.

oxygen is depleted during the run, it will be indicated by the galvanometer indicating needle, which would show the drop in terms of percentage of oxygen. It is a helpful adjunctive method to the Douglas bag procedure.

References

1. CHESKY, K., and SISE, H. S.: Use of O_2 consumption during exercise as a quantitative means of cardiac reserve. *Amer J Med,* 7:414, 1947.

2. HENDERSON, Y., and HAGGARD, H. W.: The maximum of human power and its fuel. *Amer J Physiol,* 72:264-282, 1925.

3. COLLETT, M. E., and LILJESTRAND, G.: The minute volume of the heart in man during some different types of exercise. *Scand Arch Physiol,* 45:29+, 1924.

4. BOCK, A. V.; DILL, D. B., and TALBOTT, J. H.: Determination of the rate of circulation of blood in man at work. *J Physiol,* 66:121, 1928.

5. GROLLMAN, A.: The determination of cardiac output by use of acetylene. *Amer J Physiol,* 88:432, 1929.

6. GROLLMAN, A.: *Cardiac Output of Man in Health and Disease.* Springfield, Thomas, 1932.

7. McMichael, J. *et al.*: Postural changes in cardiac output and respiration in man. *Quart J Exp Physiol, 27*:55-71, 1931.

8. Asmussen, E., and Nielsen, J.: Cardiac output during muscular work and its regulation. *Physiol Rev, 35*:778, Oct. 1955.

9. Chapman, C. B., *et al.*: Simultaneous determinations of the resting arteriovenous oxygen difference by the acetylene and direct Fick methods. *J Clin Invest, 29*:651-691, 1950.

10. Brown, H. R., and Pearson, H. R.: Demonstration of a positive relationship between cardiac output and oxygen consumption. *Proc Soc Exp Biol Med, 65*:307, June 1947.

11. Michael, E. D.: Relationship Between the Heartometer and the Acetylene Method of Measuring Circulatory Fitness. M.S. Thesis, Physical Education, U. of Ill., 1949.

12. Michael, E. D., and Cureton, T. K.: Effect of physical training on cardiac output and at 15,000 ft. simulated altitude. *Res Quart, 24*:446-452, Dec. 1953.

13. Simonsen, Ernst, and Enzer, Norbert: Physiology of muscular exercise and fatigue in disease. *Medicine (Balt), 21*:345-419, Dec. 1942.

14. Hollman, W., and Knipping, H. W.: Die Bestimmung der menschlichen Leistungsfaehigkeit vom Blickpunkt der Klinik. In *Health and Fitness in the Modern World*. Chicago, Athletic Institute (507 Merchandise Mart), 1960, pp. 17-30.

15. Balke, Bruno, and Clark, R. T.: Cardio-pulmonary and metabolic effects of physical training. In *Health and Fitness in the Modern World*, 1960, pp. 82-89.

16. Astrand, P. O.: Human physical fitness with special reference to sex and age. *Physiol Rev,* July 1956, pp. 307-335.

17. Astrand, P. O.: *Experimental Studies of Physical Working Capacity.* Copenhagen, Ejnar Munksgaard, 1952, pp. 101-136.

18. Cureton, T. K.: Treadmill tests of maximal physical efficiency. *Proc Amer Ass Health, Phys Educ and Rec,* 1950, pp. 151-154. Also in *Physical Fitness of Champion Athletes.* Urbana, U. of Ill., 1951, pp. 314-350.

19. Montoye, H. J.: Interrelations of maximal pulse rate during moderate exercise, recovery rate and post-exercise. *Res Quart, 11*:3-11, Oct. 1941.

20. DeSchriver, R. L.: Progressive Changes in the Oxygen Intake and the Oxygen Debt in Treadmill Running. M.S. Thesis, Physical Education, U. of Ill., 1955.

21. Cureton, T. K.: Cardiovascular fitness in hard athletic exercise. *J Ass Phys Ment Rehab, 12*:113-124, July-August 1958.

22. Wright, Sewell: Correlation and causation. *J Ag Res, 20*:562+, Jan. 1920.

23. Cureton, T. K.: In *Physical Fitness of Champion Athletes.* Urbana, U. of Ill., 1951, pp. 353-355.

24. Kasch, F. W.: Maximum work capacity in middle-aged males by a step test method. *J Sport Med, 5*:198-202, Dec. 1965.

25. Cureton, T. K.: Post-exercise blood pressures in maximum exertion tests and relationships to performance time, oxygen intake and oxygen debt and peripheral resistance. *J Lancet, 77*:81-82, March 1957.

26. Cotton, F. S., and Dill, D. B.: On the relation between heart rate during exercise and that of the immediate post-exercise period. *Amer J Physiol, 111*:554, 1935.

27. Morehouse, L. E., and Tuttle, W. W.: A study of the post-exercise heart rate. *Res Quart, 13*:3-9, March 1942.

28. Massey, B. H.: Changes in the Cameron Heartometer and Johnson Oscillometer Pulse Wave Tracings with Progressive Loads of Work. Ph.D. Thesis, Physical

Education, U. of Ill., 1950. Also a correlative study by Nicholas B. Strydom, Changes in Cardiac Output with Progressive Work. Ph.D. Thesis, Physical Education, U. of Ill., 1956.

29. DILL, D. B.; ROBINSON, SID, and ROSS, JOSEPH C.: A longitudinal study of 16 champion runners. *J Sport Med,* 7:4-27, March 1967.

30. RIBISL, P. M.: Effects of Training Upon the Maximal Oxygen Intake of Middle-Aged Men. Ph.D. Thesis, Physical Education, U. of Ill., 1967.

INDEX

A

Abbott, B. C., 158, 179, 181
Abboud, F. M., effect of sympatheticomimetic amines, 59, 87
Adaptation syndrome (Selye), 13, 17,.45
Adrenaline, 122, 124
Adult exercise training programs, 3-17, 13-99
All-out step test, related to oxygen intake capacity, 197, 199 (Figs. C-5, C-8), 205
All-out treadmill run, 186, 194
American Heart Association (report of Dr. Carlos Mendez, newsletter), 60
Anderson, E. C., effect of football training on BPW, 173
Approaches to health, two sides to the coin, 5
Arbeit direct body ballistocardiograph, 157 (Fig. B-32), 158, 177 (Fig. B-47), 178
Arterioles, and other small blood vessels, 40, 41, 61
Asher, Richard A., on dangers of bed rest, 21, 23
Asmussen, E., on stroke volume and Grollman method, 66, 87, 193
Astrand, P. O., 193, 206
Attinger, E. O., Editor of *Pulsatile Blood Flow*, 125, 187
Autonomic nervous system, 44, 45, 46, 48
Aviado, D. M., 83

B

Bainbridge, F., *The Physiology of Exercise*, 33, 82
Balke, Bruno, vii, 193, 206
Ballistocardiogram, or ballistocardiograph, 42, 48, 50 (Fig. 13), 75, 155, 157, 158, 161, 175, 176, 177, 179, 185
Ballisticor (ultra-low frequency), 158
Barber, Sara, experimental subject, swimming training, 158, 160
Bancroft, W. H., 151
Banister, Eric, research assistant, 158, 179, 181, 190
Bannister, Roger, 40
Barach Index, 136, 144
Barcroft, H., on the sympathetic control of blood vessels, 83

Barthels, F. H., experimental subject, 42
Barry, Alan D., assistant professor and research associate, 22, 23, 42, 47, 189
Basal metabolic rate, effect of longitudinal, progressive physical training upon, 42, 63, 66, 74, 78, 81
Basic physical fitness programs, 6-7
Beckner, G. L., and Travis Winsor, on normal physiological adaptation of the human heart to endurance work, 59
Best, C. H., 87
Birkhead, N. C., 22-3
Bishop, J. M., 23
Blanchard, H. C., experimental subject, 42
Blood volume, 42, 84
Blum, A. S., 83
Blumberger's method for determining the pre-ejection interval (ICP), 180, 186
Bock, A. V., 205
Bortz, Edward L., 55, 86
Brachial pulse wave
    effects of 6 to 8 weeks of training in progressive exercises upon, 62, 63, 64, 65, 72, 73, 74, 78, 79, 151, 152 (Figs. B-28, B-29)
    effect of a season of competitive swimming training on a top athlete, 80, 81, 82
    Ribisl's experiment, O_2 intake improvements, oxygen pulse, 75, 76
    validity coefficient (uncorrected) to predict all-out treadmill running time, 95, 158, 159
    effect of simulated altitude upon, 128
    relation of cardiac output, 134, 151, 154, 148, 149, 169
    logical analysis of, progress made, 118
    indication of shortage of myocardial oxygen supply (failure of stroke), 125, 126, 127, 128, 137-9, 169, 178, 179, 182
    in Pulse Ratio Test, 12, 18, 24, 30 and 36 steps per minute, 17-inch high bend, 126, 127
    quantitation diagram, 131
    interpretation of, 117, 129, 133, 134
    table of area/surface area, 130
    table of angles, 132

table of amplitudes after run-in-place for
one minute, 133
amplitudes with various work loads by
pedalling a bicycle ergometer, 137-9
rate of rise of the anacrotic face (velocity)
of the wave, 145-8
tourniquet effect on (application of venous
impedance), 149-50
decrement due to assuming the vertical
position, 150
area, taken as stroke volume per beat, 151,
155, 156
area used to predict 880-yard run time, 150
used to separate athletes from nonathletes,
124, 151, 153, 160, 161, 162-9
as influenced by endurance training, 151-3,
158, 160, 161, 169-75
correlated with maximal oxygen intake, 95,
151 (Fig. B-30)
damped resonance in, 151, 155, 175
related to BCG, ECG, 155, 176, 177
acceleration proportional to cardiac force
(F = Ma), 156, 158
related to initial impulse (after Rushmer)
(Ft = Mv), 155
related to training and detraining in swimming, 70-4, 157, 160 (Fig. B-35)
Cureton's improvement in six weeks of running, 3 miles per day, 172, 174
graduate theses on, completed at the University of Illinois, 173, 187 (refs. 1, 7)
changes due to exercise in various sports and
recreational activities, 174
Scientific report on by Cureton at the International Congress of Sport Medicine
and Physiology, and related sciences,
Helsinki, 1952, 173, 187 (refs. 7-8)
results of parallel recording with ECG and
BCG, 175, 176-7 (Figs. B-46, B-47)
in pathological states, 137, 175, 178-80
in some coronary cases (low acceleration,
flat type waves), 137, 181, 182-4
in 5-channel oscillographic comparisons,
179, 185-7
Brecht-Boucke capacitance transducer, 179
Brandfonbrenner, M., 33, 82, 148-9
Brassett, M., 18
Braunwald, E., 140
Brockman, S. K., 87
Brodt, M. E., effect of weight lifting training
in BPW, 173
Brown, E. W., Jr., on the shape of the brachial
pulse wave, 59, 188, 189

Brown, H. R., 206
Brown, S. R., effect of treadmill work on
BPW, 173
Brozek, Josef, 30, 32
Bruce, Robert A., 125
Bryant, F. O., effect of handball training on
BPW, 173
Bunnell, I. L., 59, 87, 125, 155, 188, 189

C

Caloric cost, calories used, 55, 57, 86
Cameron Heartometer Co., heartograph re-
search, 118, 120, 181-2, 193
Campbell, D. E., cholesterol experiment with
exercise, 53, 57, 86
Campney, H. K., effect of calisthenics and
swimming on BPW, 173
Canadian 5-BX, 10-BX Programs, 62
Capillaries, and arterioles, 21, 59, 61
Capillarization effect, increased function, new
vessels open, 41, 61, 121
Cardiovascular unfitness, 10
Carbile, Forbes, data on Australian 1960
Olympic swimmers, 48, 84, 85
Carhart, P. S., effect of underwater scuba work
on BPW, 173
Carlson, Anton, 24
Carr, P. W., 87
Cassels, D. E., 173, 203
Cattell, Raymond P., personality factors re-
lated to exercise, 29, 30
Cattell's P-technique, 155
Chailley-Bert, P., 53, 85
Chapman, C. B., 193, 206
Chen, Bambi, research assistant, 34
Chesky, K., 192, 205
Chip, W., 151, 189
Cholesterol experiments, effect of exercise,
52-6, 57, 58, 86 (ref. 144)
Christensen, E. H., on stroke volume, 66, 87,
88, 190, 193
Chronic ailments, effect of exercise upon, 8-11
Cillo, A. R., 88
Circulation, factors governing, 12, 13, 19-22, 26,
40, 44, 45, 46-7, 51, 56-7, 59-61
Clarke, R. T., 183, 206
Collett, M. E., 182, 205
Complaints of adults about poor health
(chronic ailments), 8-12
Cooper, D., 179, 181
Coronary blood flow, 59, 87 (ref. 160)
Cotton, F. S., 198, 206
Coughlan, Robert, 27, 31

Cournand needle, 127

Crampton's Blood Ptosis Test, 150

Critical flicker fusion, effects of exercise training upon, 66

Cundiff, David E., 186, 191

Crystal, D .K., 188

Cureton's progressive exercise for adults, 6-8, 10, 24, 38, 40, 83 (ref. 71)

Cureton's *Physical Fitness and Dynamic Health*, 6, 17, 83 (refs. 71, 89)

Cureton's *Physical Fitness of Champion Athletes*, 85, 130

Cureton's *Physical Fitness Appraisal and Guidance*, 130, 161, 187

Cureton's report of chronic ailments in adult men, 8-11

Cureton's 18-item Motor Fitness Test, 25, 26

Cureton's *Physical Fitness Workbook*, 24

Cureton's report on post-treadmill run diastolic pressure, 28-9

Cureton's experiment on reduction of total peripheral resistance (TPR) in middle-aged men, 36-40

Cureton's continuous, rhythmic exercice program, 38, 40, 55

Cureton's report on exercise effects on glandular functions, 55, 86

Cureton's reports on the effects of longitudinal exercise training programs on basal metabolic rate, 47, 55, 63, 64, 74, 78, 81, 86, 100

Cureton's diagram of the parallel effects of endurance exercise upon peak oxygen intake and serum cholesterol, 57 (Fig. B-44)

Cureton-Kristufek endurance running experiment, 174

Cureton-Massey experiment, limiting the supply of oxygen to human subjects in a decompression chamber to observe effect upon the ejection stroke of the heart (heartograph), 127-8, 188

Cureton's interpretations of the brachial pulse wave (heartograph), 117-87, 188

Cureton's experiment with E. Banister, B. C. Abbott and J. W. Pollard, 190

Cureton's comparison of Brandfonbrenner's stroke volume curves with age and the heartometer area stroke volume, and estimation of correction necessitated by systemic error, 149 (Fig. B-26), 188

Cureton's experiments on Roger Low, experimental subject, 77, 78

Cureton's experiment on Stuart Tuckey, experimental subject, 79

Cureton's empirical equation for estimating total peripheral resistance (TPR) from heartographs, 35-7

Cureton-Phillips experiment on middle-aged men, 62-6, 84

Cureton-Michael experiment with running training with tests at ground level and also at various simulated altitudes, 66-70, 189

Cureton-Pohndorf swimming training experiment on middle-aged men to determine the value of wheat germ oil as a supplement, 70-2, 73

Cureton-Sterling factor analysis on 104 cardiovascular variables, 190 (ref. 64)

Cureton-Wolf-Harrison swimming training experiment on middle-aged men, 72, 74

Cureton-Ribisl cross-country running experiment to improve the peak oxygen intake capacity of middle-aged men, 75-6

Cureton-Heusner swimming training experiment in hard training, 80-2

Cureton-Liverman experiments on progressive training of middle-aged men with simultaneous records of ECG, BCG and heartographs, 175-6, 177

Cureton-Banister-Abbott-Pollard experiments with middle-aged men, in physical training with testing of HGF, and first and second derivative pulse waves, 185, 190

Cureton–Du Toit experiment, comparing weight training with running, 46, 47, 187, 191

Cureton's standardization of the treadmill all-out run, 8.6% grade, 194, 206

Cureton's standardization of all-out step test, 17-inch bench, 197

Cureton's Progressive Pulse Ratio Test, 90-117

Cureton, T. K., 6, 8, 9, 10, 11, 17, 18, 23, 24, 25, 28, 31, 32, 33, 34, 35, 36, 38, 39, 40, 42, 43, 45, 46, 47, 48, 49, 53, 55, 56, 62, 66, 70, 72, 76, 80, 82, 83, 84, 85, 86, 87, 88, 89, 90, 95, 96, 99, 101, 104, 108, 118, 122, 127, 130, 133, 134, 148, 151, 152, 155, 158, 159, 161, 164 (Fig. B-38, with Jesse Owens), 166 (Fig. B-40), 170, 172, 173, 175, 176, 177, 179, 180, 181, 187, 188, 189, 190, 193, 194 (Fig. C-1, with Jesse Owens), 197, 198, 201 (Fig. C-9, with Jesse Owens), 202 (Fig. C-10, with Jesse Owens), 206

D

Daggett, W. M., on effect of vagal stimulation, 61, 87

Daly, J. W., 23

Denison, A. B., 158, 159

DeSchriver, Richard L., 206

Deterioration of circulation, 16, 19, 20, 27, 28

Deterioration of physical fitness characteristics (functions), 24-31

Deterioration of personality characteristics with age, 29-30

DeVries, Herbert A., 92, 101

Diet fortification with wheat germ oil and vitamins, minerals, 14, 70-2

Diglio, V. A., 84

Dill, D. B., 192, 193, 197, 205, 207

Diluzio, N. R., 55, 86

Donald, D. E., 85

Dontas, A. S., comparison of brachial pulse waves by cuff and venous impedance method, 127, 129, 188

Doolittle method for solving multiple regression equations, 197

Douglas bags, 82, 197, 200 (Fig. C-7)

Duggan, Nancy, 28, 30

Dunn, F. L., 48, 84, 85

Du Toit, Stephanus F., 49, 85, 88, 187

Du Toit–Cureton experiment, contrasting the physiological effects of weight training and jogging, 46, 47, 85, 88

E

ECG (electrocardiogram) effects of exercise, 64, 78, 84 (ref. 105)

Eckstein, Richard A., 179, 191

Effects of individualized programs of physical training, 15-16, 77-82, 91-100, 109-17, 158, 160, 169-72, 173, 178

Elderly subjects, tested and trained, retested, 22

Endurance exercises, 5-7

Eliasson, 61

EML (electromechanical lag) in pre-ejection period of the ECG, 48, 49, 151, 185, 186

Enzer, N., 193, 206

Eosinopenia (eosinophils), 125

Epinephrine, effect of on heart contraction (the brachial pulse wave amplitude), 60, 122, 124 (Fig. B-6)

Evans, J. I., 187

Erlanger-Hooker Index, 46, 47, 135, 140 (Fig. B-18)

Erthrocytes, changes in a season of hard competitive swimming training, 80

Exercise, as related to reducing serum cholesterol, 52-6, 57-61

Exercises, types used in basic physical training, 4-7

F

Fabre-Chevalier, experiment on exercise effects on cholesterol, 53, 85

Factors in fitness and unfitness, 8-17

Factors in cardiovascular fitness, 117-29, 137-47, 148-51, 155-6

Farhi, Asher, 37, 83, 88

Farvaar, Aghdess (Mrs. Mikkor), 88

Fatigue, 9-10, 126-8 (Figs. B-7, B-8)

Fich, S., 187

Fick method, equation for minute volume of blood flow, 193, 206 (ref. 9)

Five channel oscillograph comparisons in simultaneous recording, measuring pre-ejection intervals of the heart cycle, 178, 181, 185, 186, 187

Flicker fusion frequency, 45, 66

Forester, R. E., 23

Fox, Earl F., 134, 148, 189

Frank, K., 18

Frank, O., 125, 188

Frank-Starling mechanism, 60

Frey, Mrs. Betty, medical research technician, 119 (Figs. B-1, B-2, B-3)

Friedel, H. L., 41, 83

Fries, E. D., 155, 189

Fulton, C. D., effect of basketball training upon the BPW, 173

G

Gaderman, von E., 175, 190

Gallon, A. J., 85

Garrett, Leon, 55, 86

Geiger counter tests, 19

Gellhorn, Ernst, author of *Autonomic Imbalance and the Hypothalamus*, 44, 46, 84, 85

General resistance, 12-13

Gilmore, J. P., 87

Glick, Gerald, 190

Golding, L. A., research assistant, cholesterol experiments in progressive exercise training, 53, 54, 56, 86, 87

BPW effect of calisthenics and cross-country and handball, 5 days per week, 173

Gray, Mary D., research assistant, 101

Gregg, D. E., on sympathetic dilation of coronary arteries, 59, 87

Grollman acetylene rebreathing method for determining stroke volume, 66, 148, 149, 151, 193, 205

Grollman method, compared with other stroke volume data by Brandfonbrenner, 82, 83, 149

Gutin, Robert, 17

Guttentag, O. E., 82

H

Haggard, N. W., 205

Haldane gas analyzer, 200 (Fig. C-6)

Hall, V. E., 190

Hamilton, W. F., 125, 183, 187

Harada, Y., 87

Harris, L. G., 178, 191

Harrison, Aix B., research assistant, 72

Harrison, A. L., effect of swimming on brachial pulse wave, 173

Harrison, L. R., effect of mixed calisthenics upon BPW, 173

Harrison, Thomas R., authority on BCG and cardiovascular work, 191, 196

Hartman, F. A., 187

Harvard Step Test, 92, 101

Haskell, William S., research assistant, 119 (Figs. B-1, B-2, B-3)

Heath, W. C., 155, 189

Heath operational amplifier, 179

Heart size x-rays before and after training, 43 (Fig. 11)

Heart minute volume, relations to oxygen intake capacity, 140 (Fig. B-18), 141 (Fig. B-19), 142 (Fig. B-20), 143 (Fig. B-21), 144 (Fig. B-22), 148

Heart force, obtained on ultra-low frequency BCG (Ballisticor), showing increase in force as the result of progressive physical training (by Holloszy, Skinner, Cureton), 75

Heartometer, cutaway view, showing attachment of strain gauge to pick up motion of bellows for velocity and acceleration BCG studies, 120

Heart output
   nervous regulation of, 44-6, 48, 121
   hormonal regulation of, 56, 121

Hefner, L. L., 151, 189

Henderson, Yandell, 125, 188, 190, 205

Herxheimer, H., 42, 84

Heusner, William W., research assistant, swimming experiment, 80, 81, 82, 89

Herden, E. L., effect of walking uphill and rowing on a machine, 173

Heyman, F., comparison of intra- and extra-arterial pulse waves, 188

High gear work, 7

Hill, A. V., 192

Hill, L. T., Jr., 179, 191

Hollman, W., 193, 206

Holloszy, John, research physician, attached to Physical Fitness Research Laboratory, University of Illinois, 32, 42, 88, 124

Holmgren, A., 42, 84

Honet, J. C., 17

Hormonal regulation of cardiac output, 51, 59, 60, 122

Huggins, R. A., 151, 189

Hurxthal, L. M., 86

Husman, B. H., 16, 18

Hyman, A. S., 85, 186, 191

Hypokinetic Disease, book by Kruas and Raab, 23

I

Illinois 14-Item Test, 24

Impulse formula ($Ft = Mv$), 33

Infratron pulse signal divider, 179

Initial impulse (after Rushmer), 181

Inotropic deflection, 51

Intercorrelations of heart cycle pre-ejection intervals with other stress indicators (pH, eosinophils, oxygen debt), 51

Isovolumic contraction period (ICP), 47-51, 61, 122, 179, 181, 185, 186

J

Jebsen, R. R., 17

Johnson, E. W., 17

Johnson, R. L., 23

Johnson, T. F., 53, 56

Jokl, Ernst, 51, 85, 190

Jones, Hardin, on deterioration of circulation, (report from *Time*), 197

Jones, W. B., 151, 189

Joseph, Jack J., 9

Jungman, H., 175, 190

K

Kahn, Fritz, 12

Kapillian, Ralph H., research assistant, 17

Karfman, H. L., 179, 191

Karvonen, M. J., 189

Kasch, F. W., 198, 203, 206

Kehoe, C. L., 150, 189

Kendrick, J. E., 155, 189

Keys, Ancel, 41, 52, 82

Keys-Friedel equation, heart volume from x-ray, 83

Kireilis, Ray W., 87

Knauth, Percy, 31

Knipping, H. W., 193, 206

Knowlton, R. G., research assistant, 175

Kohelemainen, Hannes, 20

Kong, M. H., effect of swimming training upon the BPW, 173

Korobokov, A. Y., 14, 17, 18

Kraus, Hans, 22, 23

Kristufek, Charles J., 170, 171, 174

Kritchevsky, D., book on cholesterol, 55, 86

Kroeker, E. J., 129, 188

Krogh, August, book on capillaries, 83 (ref. 82)

Kruzic, W. M., effect of mixed activities upon the BPW, 173

Krzywanek, H. J., 32

Kummerow, Fred A., diagram of cholesterol metabolism, 57, 58

Kurbatov, T., 40, 83

L

LaBaw, N. L., effect of basketball training on BPW, 173

Landowne, M., 40, 82, 83, 148, 189

Leukocyte count, 136

Liljestrand, G., 205

Lindgren, P., 61, 87

Liverman, Robert D., research assistant, 175, 176, 177, 180

Losses, due to discontinuing training, 46, 57, 62, 64, 65

Linden, R. J., 87

Ling, J. S. L., 83

Low Gear Work, 7

Lowe, Roger, experimental subject, 42

Lucksinger, P. C., 155, 189

M

MacLeay, Jesse, experiment on blood flow in various levels of work, 134 (Figs. B-12, B-14)

Mann, G. V., 54, 55, 86, 87

Marcotte, G. E., effect of the skating training upon the BPW, 173

Marshall, John, 22

Marshall, R. J., 149, 189

Massey, B. H., 127, 133, 134, 135 (Fig. B-13), 148, 188, 206

Master, A. M., 125

Masuda, Makoto, 83

Mateef, Dragomir, 14, 18, 87

McAdam, Robert E., research assistant, 36, 83, 204 (Fig. C-11)

McDonald, D. A., 188

McMichael, J., recommends modifications in the Grollman method, 66, 88, 193, 206

Mendez, C. D., effect of epinephrine upon heart stroke (report of the American Heart Association), 60

Mental excitement, stimulation of sympathetic nervous system, 51

Métevier, J. Guy, research assistant, 53, 86

Metzner, A., 175, 178

Michael, E. D., Jr., research assistant, 96, 148, 189, 206

Michael-Cureton Chart (for determining proportionate stroke volume from heartographs), 35, 82, 148

Michael-Cureton track training experiment at ground level with testing both at ground level and at 10,000 feet of simulated altitude, and changes in stroke volume and cardiac output, 66-70, 148-9, 189, 206

Middle-aged men, summary of effects of exercise training upon, 19-22, 61

Middle-gear work, 7

Miles, Walter, 30

Minute volume, variations in training and detraining, 66, 68, 140, 141, 142, 143, 144, 148, 195

Mitchell, Jere H., 59, 87

Montoye, Henry J., 53, 86, 101, 147, 206

Morehouse, L. E., 198, 206

Mueller, G. W., 84

N

Nagle, F., 84

Nakamura, P. K., effect of swimming training upon the BPW, 173

National Institutes of Health, 148

Naughton, John, 42, 84

Nervous regulation of heart output, 49, 51, 59, 60, 61, 121-5

Nielsen, J., 193, 206

Nielsen, M., 87

Noble, Bruce, research assistant and assistant professor, 196 (Fig. C-3)

Norris, A. H., 17

Nugent, G. C., 87

Nyberg's electrical impedance method, 127

O

Ogawa, Y., 40, 83

Ogden, E., 82

Olsen, K. J., 17

Olson, Edith V., 23

Orban, William, research assistant, 202 (Fig. C-10, with Cureton and Jesse Owens)

Osborn, Harold, 204 (Fig. C-11, with R. E. McAdam), 205 (Fig. C-12, with R. E. McAdam)

Oscillometer (Johnson's type), 134 (Fig. B-12), 135

Owens, Jesse, being tested with heartometer, 164 (Fig. B-38), 194 (Fig. C-1), 201 (Fig. C-4), 202 (Fig. C-10)

Oxygen intake, in training and during detraining, 81, 82, 113, 171

Oxygen intake, taken progressively during a season of competitive swimming training, 81, 82

Oxygen intake and oxygen debt, taken progressively during the pulse ratio test at 12, 18, 24, 30 and 36 steps per minute, 113-15 (Figs. A-16, A-17, A-20)

Oxygen debt, 61, 113, 114, 115, 117, 192

P

Page, H. F., 23

Page, Irving H., 45, 86

Pallandi, Taimo, experiment on TPR, 38, 83

Pangle, R. V., 55, 87

Parallel effects of endurance exercise upon cholesterol and peak oxygen intake capacity, 56, 57

Payne, J. H., 179, 191

Parasympathetic nervous system, effect of training upon, 44

Pearson, H. R., 206

Peripheral resistance (TPR), 33, 35-40

Petrén, T., 40, 88

Phillips, E. E., research assistant, effects of calisthenics, running and handball before the BPW, 173

Phillips, Earl E., 62-5, 79

Phillips-Cureton training experiment with middle-aged men, 84, 85, 88

Pihkala, Lauri, 17

Ph, changes in a season of competitive swimming training, 82, 89, 196

Physical fitness and dynamic health, 6, 30

Physical training effects, 15-17, 22, 33-89, 111, 112, 151-3, 158, 160, 170-9

Physiological objectives, 3, 4

Physiological failure, aging, 32

Pohndorf, R. H., experiment on swimming to reduce cholesterol, 70-3, 75, 196

Pohndorf, effect of swimming upon the BPW, 173

Pollard, J. W., 158, 181

Polyethylene serial bags for collection of expired gas, 200

Postexercise pulse rate, related to other stress indicators, 51

Positive dynamic health through exercise and rhythmic living, 5

Potassium, effect upon the vigor of the heart stroke, 60

Powers, B. S., 55, 86, 87

Precordial R and T-waves of the electrocardiogram, 62-4

Pre-ejection intervals of the heart stroke cycle, 47, 49 (Figs. 12, 13), 51, 185 (Figs. B-53, B-54)

Progressive Pulse Ratio Test, 89-197

Progressive physical training, effects on the cardiovascular system, 57, 62-81, 111-12, 151-3, 160-77

Pressure programs, some danger for adults out of condition, 61, 88 (ref. 174)

Pressure pulse waves, sophisticated mathematical analyses, 125

Pulse rate, relations to minute volume in submaximal work, 142

Q

Quimby, C. W., Jr., 83

R

Raab, Wilhelm, 22, 23, 32, 51, 85, 180, 181

Raab, Wilhelm, editor of *Prevention of Ischemic Heart Disease,* 29

Ralston, H. J., 33, 83

Randall, W. C., effect of sympathetic stimulation on vigor of the heart stroke, 62, 88

Ray, Joie, 22

Reduction of total peripheral resistance in middle-aged adults, 36-41

Reindell, H. H., 42, 84

Remington, J. W., 187

Resistance to stress, 12

Rhythmic exercises, effect of on heart size, 42-4

Ribisl, Paul M., experiment on improving oxygen intake by endurance running with middle-aged men, 42, 75-6, 84, 89, 204

Ring, G. C., 83

Robinson, Sid, graph of oxygen intake capacity at various ages, 76, 203, 206

Rochelle, R. H., experiment on running to reduce cholesterol, 53, 86

Rodahl, Kaare, 23

Rodbard, S., index of stroke output, QRS to first heart sound, 61, 88, 186-7, 191

Rohse, W. G., effect of sympathetic stimulation on vigor of the heart beat, 62, 88

Rose, K. D., 48, 84, 85

Ross, Joseph C., 207

RQ (respiratory quotient), variations in training and detraining, 68, 69

Running versus weight training programs, effects on the cardiovascular, 46, 47

Rushmer, Robert, on cardiac dynamics, "the initial impulse," 125, 158, 181, 187, 188, 190, 191

Ryan, R. L., effect of wrestling training upon BPW, 173

S

Sarnoff, S. J., on contractility of the heart, 60, 87

Scarborough, W. R., 50

Schmidt, C. F., 83

Selye, Hans, 13, 14, 17, 32

Selye's Principles of adaptation to stress, 17 (refs. 13-16), 45

Selye's common basis of disease, 28, 29

Serum cholesterol, effects of longitudinal physical training upon, 52-61, 62

Shepherd, J. T., 149, 189

Sherman, Michael, laboratory assistant, 200 (Fig. C-6)

Shipley, R. E., 59, 87

Shock, Nathan W., 17, 77, 82, 148, 189

Simonsen, Ernst, 193, 206

Sjöstramd, T., 83

Skinner, J. S., research assistant, 55, 75, 86, 88

Skinner, Holloszy, Barry, Cureton, training experiments on middle-aged men, 75

Sloninger, E. L., research assistant, 85, 181, 186, 187, 191

Snell, R. E., 155, 189

Snyder, Julian, 31

Specific effects of physical training, 33-82

Spencer, M. P., 151, 189

Spicer, W. S., 23

Stallman, Robert K., 88

Starr, Isaac, 27, 36, 81

Starr, I., and F. C. Wood, 27 (Fig. 3), 52

Starr, I., and S. Ogawa, 156 (Figs. B-31a, B-31b)

Steinman, R. R., 18

Steinmetz, J. R., 23

Sterling, Leroy F., 155, 190
longitudinal effect of badminton playing upon the BPW, 173

Stress effects, 12, 13, 40, 45-51, 58-61

Strength, 15, 35 (Fig. B-13), 46

Strydom, Nicolaas P., research assistant, 134, 135, 189

Stroke volume
effects of exercise training, 65-70, 151
from heartograph area or amplitude, 148-53
Michael-Cureton conversion chart, 35 (Fig. 8)
variations in training and detraining, 62-5
effect of a season of competitive swimming training, 80-2

Substitute (simplified) methods of testing to estimate oxygen intake capacity, 84, 95, 140-8, 154 (Fig. B-30), 195, 197

Swan, H. J. C., 83, 189

Swollen joints, 8

Sylvan, B., 83

Sympathetic nervous stimulation, 60-2

Sympatho-adrenergic stimulation of heart stroke, 60-2, 121-5

Sympathetic nervous system, effects of progressive training, 44-8, 49-51

Systolic blood pressure, in training and detraining, 63, 67

T

Talbot, S. A., 50

Talbott, J. H., 192, 205

Tanner, Lauri, 42, 84

Tartaryn, P., 18

Taylor, N. B., 87

Tenckhoff, H. A., 17

Tensing exercise, effects of, 39-41, 44-8, 88 (ref. 174)

Tension period of heart cycle (TP), 48, 49, 50, 51, 122, 179-81, 185, 186

Tigerstedt Index, 136, 143

The Healthy Life (Life-Time book), 24, 30, 32

Total peripheral resistance, 33, 35-7
table of calculated values, 37
implications of, 38-40

Trained state, the value of, 14-16
Tuckey, S. L., experimental subject, 36, 38
    improvement in cardiovascular condition,
        79 (Fig. 22), 80
Tuma, J. W., effect of 26 weeks of underwater
    and demolition training upon the BPW,
    173
Tuttle, W. W., 198
T-waves, of the telemetered electrocardiogram,
    48

U

Ungerleider-Clark table of heart size, 41, 80, 83
Uvnas, B., 59, 61, 83, 87, 167

V

Validity coefficients of submaximal tests to
    predict all-out treadmill performance, 95
Val Salva effect, 59, 125
Van Huss, Wayne D., 53, 133
Velocity, from brachial pulse wave, rate of rise,
    121, 145
Venous impedance, 149-50
Vincitore, Michael A., 101
Volume elasticity, E., 36
Von E. Gadermann, comparison of brachial
    pulse waves, 175, 190

W

Wagner, I. H., 17
Walker, E. D., experimental subject, 22, 123
    (ref. 40)
Walker, H. G., 4, 187
Wang, Y., 149, 189
Warm-up, effect of Progressive Pulse Ratio
    Test, 95, 96, 97, 98, 99
Warm-up exercises, 5, 6
Warner, H. R., 151, 189
Weber, Herbert, research assistant, 187, 191
Weight deviation with age (after Brozek), 30
    (Fig. 6)
Weight training, effects of, 46
Weissler, A. M., 178, 191

Wells, Harold P., effect of calisthenics upon
    the BPW, 173
Wells, J. B., 51, 85, 190
Wheat germ oil, with training experiments,
    14, 17 (ref. 18), 19, 64-7, 73 (Fig. 20)
White, G. D., 178, 191
White, Paul D., 22
White, William H. (with T. K. Cureton),
    exercise for adults, 17
Wieth-Pedersen, G., 87
Wiggers, Carl J., book on *Circulatory Dynam-
    ics*, 33, 82, 83, 125, 178, 187, 188, 190, 191
Willcutt, R. B., 175, 190
Willett, E., research assistant, 159 (Fig. C-4)
Williams, John C. P., 151, 187, 189, 191
Wilson, A. L., effect of weight lifting upon
    the BPW, 173
Winsor, T., 179, 191
Wittich, G. H., 18
Wolbers, C. P., 173, 174
Wolf, Jacob G., research assistant, swimming
    training experiment, 72
Wolffe, Joseph B., 32, 84
Wolfson, M., effect of prescribed exercise upon
    the BPW, 173, 174
Wolkowitz, W., 187
Wong, H. Y. C., 53, 86
Wood, Earl H., 129, 150, 167, 168, 169, 187
Wood, F. C., 27, 87, 119, 179, 191
World Health Organization, 88
Wren, E. A., 149, 189
Wright, Sewall, path coefficient (Beta weight)
    system, 36, 197, 206

Y

Y.M.C.A., adult fitness programs, clinics, 8

Z

Zatopec, Emil, 20
Zimkin, N. Y., effect of physical training to
    resist stress, 14, 17, 18, 88